How To Know
THE FRESHWATER FISHES

Pictured-Keys for identifying all of the freshwater
fishes of the United States and also including a number of marine species which often enter freshwater.

by

SAMUEL EDDY, Ph.D.

Professor of Zoology

UNIVERSITY OF MINNESOTA

WM. C. BROWN COMPANY
Publishers
DUBUQUE, IOWA

Copyright 1957
by
H. E. Jaques

Library of Congress Catalog Card Number: 58-3084

THE PICTURED-KEY NATURE SERIES

"How to Know the Insects," Jaques, 1947

"Living Things—How to Know Them," Jaques, 1946

"How to Know the Trees," Jaques, 1946

"Plant Families—How to Know Them," Jaques, 1948

"How to Know the Economic Plants," Jaques, 1948, 1958

"How to Know the Spring Flowers," Cuthbert, 1943, 1949

"How to Know the Mosses and Liverworts," Conard, 1944, 1956

"How to Know the Land Birds," Jaques, 1947

"How to Know the Fall Flowers," Cuthbert, 1948

"How to Know the Immature Insects," Chu, 1949

"How to Know the Protozoa," Jahn, 1949

"How to Know the Mammals," Booth, 1949

"How to Know the Beetles," Jaques, 1951

"How to Know the Spiders," Kaston, 1952

"How to Know the Grasses," Pohl, 1953

"How to Know the Fresh-Water Algae," Prescott, 1954

"How to Know the Western Trees," Baerg, 1955

"How to Know the Seaweeds," Dawson, 1956

"How to Know the Freshwater Fishes," Eddy, 1957

"How to Know the Weeds," Jaques, 1959

"How to Know the Water Birds," Jaques-Ollivier, 1960

"How to Know the Butterflies," Ehrlich, 1961

"How to Know the Eastern Land Snails," Burch, 1962

"How to Know the Grasshoppers," Helfer, 1963

"How to Know the Cacti," Dawson, 1963

Other Subjects in Preparation

Printed in U.S.A.

CONTENTS

FOREWORD

HESE keys for the identification of freshwater fishes of the United States were originally prepared for the use of the author's class in Ichthyology at the University of Minnesota. The original keys have been tested repeatedly with actual specimens by many generations of students. The keys cover all the fishes of the United States which are regarded as strictly freshwater species, and also include a number of marine species which often enter freshwater. The number of marine fishes which may enter the mouths of rivers is so great that only part of them are included here.

For years the writer has hesitated to publish these keys because of the uncertain taxonomic position of many species. For a long time the names and specific relations of many fishes have shifted back and forth. The writer finally concluded that the classification of fishes will continue to undergo changes and there was no reason for waiting. Consequently, these keys have been prepared to aid in the identification of most fishes, but for some species there may be changes even while this book is in press. There are some doubtful species which remain to be cleared up whenever a special study is made of the group. Therefore, a key of this nature is an instrument for the present, and future changes may be expected.

The writer has tried to make this key as elementary as possible and to avoid unnecessary technical terms. There is no pretense to form a natural arrangement, and the species are arranged in the order in which they key out most easily. The family arrangement with several exceptions follows the order of Berg. The keys follow a dichotomous form. They are arranged in couplets, each part of a couplet consisting of a set of opposing characters. Each part of a couplet ends with the number of the continuing couplet for the next step, eventually leading to the couplet, one of which ends with the name of the proper family, genus or species. The beginner should start with the family key and follow the couplets according to the characters which agree with those of his fish until he arrives at the family. He should then turn to the key for that family and follow the key until he arrives at the genus and species.

The writer is responsible for all illustrations, and with few exceptions has prepared them from actual specimens. The writer wishes to acknowledge his appreciation to his wife, Vera C. Eddy, who has helped him throughout the preparation of this book. He is greatly indebted to the large number of colleagues from all parts of the United

States who have generously contributed specimens to the collections of the University of Minnesota, and which have been used in the preparation of these keys. Many of his graduate students have helped by testing the keys during various stages of their preparation. He is especially indebted to Dr. R. M. Bailey, University of Michigan; Dr. E. A. Lachner, U. S. National Museum; Dr. R. D. Ross, Virginia Polytechnic Institute; and Dr. R. D. Suttkus, Tulane University for aid in the preparation of this book.

Minneapolis, Minnesota

Samuel Eddy

Fish rank very high as a source of food for man and contribute much for us in a recreational way. Biologically they represent the oldest vertebrates and have a very distinct place in the life history chain of plants and animals.

We are much indebted to Doctor Eddy for his knowledge, skill and patience in producing this book. His drawings are outstanding. Some species are pictured for the first time.

SOME FACTS ABOUT FISHES

 ISHES represent the largest division of the vertebrates. Many fossil fishes are known which were very primitive and are considered as the earliest vertebrates. From some of these the modern fishes have descended. Modern fishes, although containing a few relicts of these ancient groups, are mostly highly modernized forms as well adapted for their mode of life as land animals are for a terrestrial life. In fact, some fishes show more highly developed and more specialized structures than any of the other vertebrates. Flying forms have developed. In many groups luminescent structures and powerful electric organs have appeared.

The fishes living today can be divided into the cyclostomes or round mouth eels *(Agnatha)*, the cartilaginous fishes *(Chondrichthyes)*, and the bony fishes (Osteichthyes). The cyclostomes are found in both freshwater and the sea, and are offshoots of the earliest types of vertebrates known. While they are primitive in that they have never developed the teeth, upper and lower jaws, paired appendages or fins, the living cyclostomes are highly specialized for a semi-parasitic life. The cartilaginous fishes also represent the modern descendants of an early group and today consist mainly of

Pteraspis, an early fossil fish

the sharks, skates, and rays. In the United States these are all marine and only a few occasionally wander into the mouths of rivers. These are not included in this book. The bony fishes constitute the greatest group of living fishes populating the freshwaters and seas of the world with all types including many highly diversified forms.

The bony fishes include a few primitive forms, the superorders Chondrostei and Holostei, which are relicts of the earliest bony fishes and are found mostly in the freshwaters of the United States. Except for a few cyclostomes, all the other freshwater fishes of the United States are modern bony fishes of the superorder Teleostei.

Most of the fishes in our inland waters are restricted to freshwater and cannot live in the sea. Fishes which spend most of their lives in freshwater but go to the sea to spawn, are known as *catadromous* fishes. The only common catadromous fish in the United States is the

1

American eel. Fishes which spawn in freshwater, but spend most of their lives in the sea, are known as *anadromous* fishes. Many fishes, such as, the Pacific salmon, some shad and smelt spend most of their lives in the sea, but regularly enter freshwater to spawn. These are considered as freshwater fishes in this book. Some freshwater fishes, such as the trout, have anadromous races which commonly go to sea, but return to freshwater for spawning.

I am anadromous and must hurry home to spawn

Some freshwater families have species which often invade the brackish or sea water at the mouths of rivers, but never venture far into the sea. Some of the salt water fishes frequently invade the freshwater at the mouths of rivers and some may penetrate upstream for several hundred miles. In this book some of the marine fishes which commonly invade freshwater are included, but the number occasionally entering freshwater is so great that it would make the keys too cumbersome to include all marine fishes that have been reported from freshwater.

The freshwater fishes of the United States do not reach the enormous size attained by many of the marine fishes or by some of the freshwater fishes in other parts of the world. A weight of several hundred pounds may be reached by some catfishes and the lake sturgeon. The anadromous white sturgeon of the Pacific northwest has been reported weighing over 1000 pounds. Several of our freshwater fishes are quite minute seldom exceeding an inch in length such as gambusia, the pygmy sunfish, and the least killifish.

DISTRIBUTION AND CONDITIONS FOR EXISTENCE

The distribution of fishes is usually determined by stream systems as land divides often constitute an effective barrier. The greatest separation of American fishes is caused by the continental divide which rather effectively has separated the fishes of the Pacific drainage from those of the Atlantic drainage. In most cases entirely different species and even genera occur on the two sides of the divide. A few species have crossed apparently at the narrow divide between the headwaters of the Missouri and Columbia Rivers. The Arctic and the Great Lakes drainages have had many connections with the Mississippi drainage and, consequently, show many species common to both. Several fishes found in the Arctic drainage have penetrated into the northern part of the Mississippi drainage, but are probably restricted from going farther south because of suitable living conditions. The Atlantic drainage shows that many fishes from the Mississippi drainage have been able to cross the divide, but there are many species which are restricted to the streams of the Atlantic seaboard. In some cases these are continuous in the coastal streams along the Gulf of Mexico.

There are many cases of isolated stream systems containing endemic species, such as, stream systems of the southwestern desert which have lost all connections with other basins and empty into lakes without any outlets. Also coastal rivers, such as the Sacramento and many rivers in southeastern United States, are isolated and have developed partially endemic fish faunas.

Many fishes show individual preferences for certain water conditions and are to a certain extent restricted in their distribution by these conditions. Some fishes, such as members of the salmon family, are restricted to cold waters and will not be encountered in regions where there are no waters within their optimum range of temperature. Other fishes prefer warmer waters, such as black basses and sunfishes, and thrive best in waters which reach temperatures above 75°. The various ciscoes, the Great Lakes whitefish, the lake trout, and a few other fishes are restricted to lake waters and avoid streams. Other fishes prefer running waters and are more likely to be found in rivers. Certain darters are found only in small swift streams. Fishes, such as the larger catfishes, are more likely to be found in the larger and more placid rivers. Land barriers between stream systems are not the only condition limiting the range of a fish, as the proper habitat conditions for that particular species must also be present.

Fishes depend on many other conditions for their existence, but fortunately many of these conditions, such as food, are ample in most freshwaters. If the salt content is too great, as in Great Salt Lake, it will prevent any fish from living there, but in most waters the salt content is within the tolerance for most fishes. The carbonate or lime concentration, although important to the growth of food organisms, is usually within the tolerance of fishes. Proper spawning beds are a very important factor and often form a limiting factor as most fishes need certain depths, bottom types and water temperatures for spawning, and without these conditions they cannot maintain the species.

A necessary factor in the existence of fishes is the presence of sufficient oxygen for respiration. Fishes obtain their oxygen from that dissolved in the water and cannot live when this falls below a certain

concentration. Some shallow waters in the north may develop an insufficient amount of oxygen during the winter. Much of the oxygen in standing water originates from the oxygen given off by aquatic plants during photosynthesis. When sunlight is cut off by snow on the ice, the photosynthesis stops, and the shallow lakes may lose most or all of their dissolved oxygen. Streams obtain most of their oxygen from the atmosphere as the flowing water rolls along and rubs against the air. Consequently, streams usually do not show as much winter oxygen reduction. An important contributing factor to oxygen reduction is the decomposition of organic matter. An abundance of organic matter, such as a heavy weed crop or even domestic sewage through the oxidation processes of decomposition causes a great oxygen consumption and often results in depletion of the oxygen. This is one of the chief reasons why pollution renders water unfit for fishes.

In many of the deep northern lakes, the cold water stratifies in summer and remains below the warmer surface water and is too deep for photosynthetic activity. If considerable organic matter has settled into this deep water, oxidation may soon deplete the oxygen from the lower levels and cause the fishes to be confined to the upper levels. Only those deep lakes which are not fertile enough to produce much plant life have sufficient oxygen to maintain fishes in their lower levels. Large lakes with strong currents may keep the water sufficiently stirred to prevent any stagnation.

ACTIVITIES

Most fishes feed on or close to the bottom and hence are restricted to water where they can always reach the bottom. A few fishes are pelagic and live in the deep open waters of large lakes. These feed chiefly on plankton or other fishes which are in turn plankton feeders. Fishes exhibit all sorts of feeding habits. Young fishes when first hatched usually start feeding on the minute crustacea which swarm in the shallow water. Many soon turn to small insects and fry of other fishes. Many of the minnows, bullheads, and other rough fishes consume large quantities of plant food. A few fishes are plankton feeders, possessing fine gill rakers by which they strain out the tiny crustacea and other planktonic forms which swarm through the open waters of all lakes. The game fishes are mostly predaceous, feeding on smaller fishes and on all sorts of other aquatic animal life. Thus long chains of food habits are established. The forage fishes feeding on plants and on plankton, furnish food for the predaceous fishes which top the chain. Suckers sweep over the bottom with their sucker mouths utilizing anything that is edible. In between are the insectivorous fishes, such as crappies, sunfishes, and perch, feeding mainly on the smaller animal life, but occasionally feeding on small fishes and in turn sometimes eaten by the larger game fishes.

Fishes exhibit definite working hours as do most animals. Some are diurnal and start their activities after sunup. Others are nocturnal and are most active at night. Night feeders usually have keen sense of taste and smell by which they partly or wholly locate their food. Diurnal fishes usually locate their food by taste and sight and some, such as the pike, use sight almost entirely.

Many fishes are gregarious and tend to keep together in "schools." Others, such as the adult pike and black basses, are solitary. The black basses for the first six months of their lives are gregarious, but they soon separate and each male more or less selects his own territory which he defends against all invaders. The related sunfishes remain gregarious, and even when spawning are so sociable that they may put their nests as close together as possible. Bullheads are gregarious and swarm in schools.

Fishes exhibit several types of definite movements. The spawning runs of many are well known. The suckers and the walleyes follow definite paths to their spawning beds at the start of each spring. The mad crowding rush of the Pacific salmon, smelt, shad, and many other anadromous fishes to their spawning beds are well known classic examples. Less spectacular are the spawning runs of many of our freshwater fishes, such as those of the suckers.

We are just beginning to learn about the daily movements of many of our common fishes. Pike move into the shallow waters during the day to feed and at evening pass to the deeper waters outside of the weed beds to spend the night. On the other hand, the pike-perch move inshore at sundown and spend the night in shallow water moving outside the weed beds during the early morning to spend the day. Perch and sunfishes also exhibit similar daily movements. Each kind of fish seems to have worked out a definite pattern of activity which may vary with the age of the fish.

REPRODUCTION

Fishes are usually very prolific breeders, producing enormous numbers of eggs which compensate for the numerous hazzards to which the eggs and young are exposed. The number of eggs produced per fish may vary from 15 to 20 as in some live-bearers to over

a million as in the carp and eel. Most fishes produce eggs which are fertilized and hatched after they are laid. A few, such as the members of the family Poeciliidae, are live-bearers, giving birth to the living young. In this case the eggs are retained in the oviduct where they are fertilized by sperm introduced by the male. The eggs develop and actually hatch within the mother who thus gives birth to living young. In these fishes the number of eggs are few, but the chance of survival is great.

The majority of our freshwater fishes are egg-laying and have developed two methods for developing the eggs. One method, and perhaps the most common, is that of depositing the eggs at random on suitable but unprepared spawning beds. The eggs are fertilized as they are laid by one or more attending males and are left to develop and hatch without any further care. These random spawners produce enormous numbers of eggs, often many thousands or more. A number of our fishes, such as sunfishes and catfishes, are nest builders and prepare a nest, usually a cleared depression where the female deposits the eggs which are then guarded by the male who also guards the young fry for some time afterwards. These fishes usually produce only a few thousand eggs, and the chance for survival is much greater than in the random spawners. There are a number of fishes that have partial nesting habits, depositing the eggs in a prepared nest and even guarding the eggs but giving no care to the young. Many minnows prepare nests and some even guard the eggs. Many trout make some preparation covering their eggs with gravel and then leaving the eggs to shift for themselves.

STRUCTURE OF A FISH*

 N ORDER to identify a fish it is necessary to know some-thing about the structure of a fish especially those parts used in classification. The shape of fishes vary greatly. Many have slender streamlined bodies, but others develop thick heavy bodies, fitting almost every conceivable dimension. Some may be very long and cylindrical as in the eel, others are compressed laterally and are deep vertically as in the sunfishes. Proportions vary greatly. Some fishes have large wide heads and small slender bodies, while others may have smal! heads with wide heavy bodies.

The general terms of anatomical dimensions apply to fishes the same as to other animals. *Anterior* refers to before or to the front end or part of the body or structure. *Posterior* refers to behind or to the hind end or part of the body or structure. *Dorsal* refers to the back or upper surface. *Ventral* refers to the under part or lower surface. *Lateral* means the sides or toward the sides. *Medial* refers to the central part or middle of the body or structure.

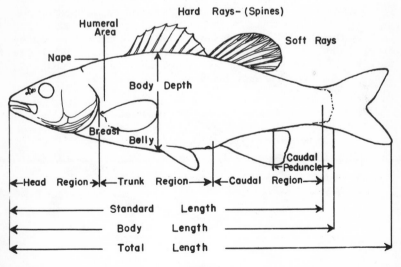

Figure 1

*The cyclostomes represented by the lampreys (page 28) form a type whose struc-ture is more primitive in many ways than that of the other fishes and, consequently, the following description applies to the bony fishes.

7

The body of a fish is divided into three regions, consisting of *head, trunk,* and *caudal* regions (Fig. 1). No neck is present, although the region of the back just behind the head is called the *nape.* The head is that part extending to the posterior edge of the gill cover or *opercle.* The trunk is the region from the edge of the *opercle* to the anus. Several areas may be found in the trunk. The *pectoral* (shoulder) area is that just behind the opercle and includes the *humeral* area which is the area just above the base of the pectoral fin. The *abdomen* or *belly* is the extreme ventral portion between the pectoral fins and the anus. The *thorax* or *breast* is the ventral area immediately in front of the pectoral fins.

The *tail* or *caudal* region (Fig. 1) is the region from behind the anus extending to the caudal fin, and is not the caudal or tail fin. The more or less slender part of the caudal region behind the anal or dorsal fin (whichever extends farthest back) and extending to the base of the caudal fin is the *caudal peduncle.* The anus (Fig. 2) is the posterior opening of the digestive tract and is adjacent to the openings of the urogenital tracts. The general area of the anus is often swollen.

Fishes possess several kinds of fins, which are usually membranous structures supported by rays or spines. Rays are modified into soft and hard rays. *Soft rays* (Fig. 1) are slender flexible structures composed of many bony joints and are typically split or divided at their outer ends. The soft rays at the front of a fin are usually short and are not divided at their tips and are known as *rudimentary soft rays* (Fig. 2). When counts of the fin rays are made, the short rudimentary rays are not included, but the long unbranched ray usually found at the front of the dorsal and anal fins is usually included in the count. The last soft ray of both dorsal and anal fins is often split almost to the base and may be mistaken for two rays.

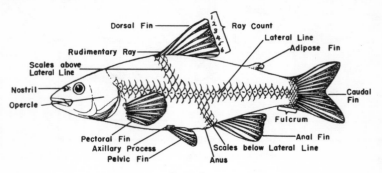

Figure 2

8

In a few fishes, such as the catfishes and the European carp, groups of soft rays may fuse into a stiff spine-like structure known as *hard rays*. These are usually barbed. If their membranous covering is removed their jointed structure will be detected. *True spines* (Fig. 1) are stiff rays ending in sharp points and do not show a jointed structure.

The median or un-paired fins of a fish consist of the dorsal, caudal, and anal fins. The *dorsal fin* (Fig. 2) extends along the middle of the back and may be divided into several parts, the anterior portion often

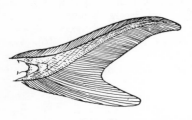

being spiny. The tail terminates in the *caudal fin* which has developed several types. Primitive fishes or relics of ancient groups have a *heterocercal* type (Fig. 3) in which the vertebral column extends out into the upper lobe of the fin. A modification of this type (See Fig. 14) occurs in the Families Amiidae and Lepisosteidae, where the young are hatched with typical heterocercal fins, but lose the up-

Figure 3

per lobe as they grow. Most fishes have a *homocercal* type (Fig. 4) of caudal fin where the vertebral column ends at the base of the fin. This type may be forked, rounded, or square. The caudal fin is composed of soft rays with rudimentary rays on each side. The term *fulcrum* (Fig. 2) applies to the swollen area above and below the base of the caudal fin produced by the continuation of the rudimentary rays.

The *anal fin* (Fig. 2) is a median ventral fin located just posterior to the anus. It may be composed of both spines and soft rays. The shape of the anal and dorsal fins is usually not highly variable, but sometimes one or both of these fins may

Figure 4

assume a *falcate* (sickle-shape) form (Fig. 5) with an "S" shape edge.

Fins corresponding to arms and legs are present on most fishes, although one or both pairs are lost in a few fishes. The anterior pair

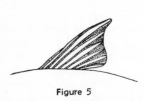

Figure 5

of fins are the *pectoral fins* (Fig. 2) located laterally on the shoulder girdle just back of the *opercle*. The *pelvic fins* (Fig. 2) are typically located just anterior to the anus, but in many fishes they move forward. When the pelvic fins are near the anus, they are termed abdominal in position (See Fig. 21), but when they are near or under the pectorals they are termed thoracic in position (See Fig. 22). In some species they may be anterior to the pectoral fins and are termed jugular in position. In many fishes slender ridges or structures known as *axillary processes* (Fig. 2) are found in the angles at the base of the pelvic fins.

Another type of fin found in some fishes is the *adipose fin* (Fig. 2) characteristic of trout, catfishes and several other groups. This is a small median fin behind the dorsal fin distinguished by being a soft fleshy structure without any rays or spines.

The body of a fish is ordinarily more or less covered with *scales:* Sometimes the scales are so small they can barely be detected. Areas without scales are usually said to be naked. A few fishes have lost their scales entirely. Scales are of several types. Several of the most primitive bony fishes possess hard rhomboid or diamond shape scales which do not overlap and are called *ganoid scales* (Fig. 6). Many

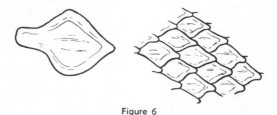

Figure 6

primitive fishes also have heavy bony plates on the body covering the heads. In the teleost fishes the bony plates of the head have been incorporated with the internal skeleton and are not easily discernable.

Two types which are really modifications of the same scale are found in the higher bony fishes. Each scale is a thin shingling disc of bone with the exposed part covered by a very thin skin. The scale is formed by concentric layers of bone (circuli) which are laid down at the margin of the scale as the fish grows. During the winter when growth ceases or is retarded, the scale may suffer some re-absorption at the margin. When growth is resumed in the spring this causes a distinct mark known as an annulus which is used to determine the age of the fish. Ridges appearing as lines radiate out from the center of the scale and are known as *radii*. The simple smooth scales are the *cycloid type* (Fig. 7). *Ctenoid scales* (Fig. 8) are similar, but are differentiated by tiny spines covering the exposed portion. Frequently the scale must be removed and magnified to determine the structure. Scales are usually restricted or may be absent on the head. In some fishes the scales may be absent from the nape, belly and breast. The scales are

Figure 7

counted on various parts of the body for identification (see page 14 for various counts). Some scales are modified as the enlarged scales on the mid-belly of some darters. Many darters and some killifishes have an

enlarged *humeral scale* located just behind the opercle and above the base of the pectoral fin. The thin skin of fishes contains numerous mucous glands which keep the skin covered with a slime which is protective, preventing bacteria and moulds from infecting the delicate skin.

Figure 8

The head of a fish includes the gill region which corresponds to the neck and throat region of higher animals. The fleshy part of the head before the eye and above the mouth is the *snout* (Fig. 9). Its length is determined as the distance from the front or tip to the anterior margin of the orbit. This part contains the *nostrils* which are primarily a pair of blind pits and function only as smell organs. Each nostril aperture is divided by a flap or fleshy partition into an incurrent and excurrent opening (Fig. 9). The upper jaws under the snout are formed of bones covered by skin and a thin layer of flesh except in a few fishes which develop fleshy lips. The upper jaw (Fig. 9) consists of several pairs of bones.

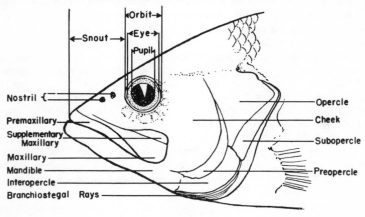

Figure 9

The front and outer pair is the *premaxillaries* which may be separated from the snout by a distinct groove (See Fig. 200) in which case they are termed *protractile*. If a bridge of flesh crosses the groove and connects the premaxillaries to the snout (See Fig. 201), they are termed *non-protractile*. The *maxillary* (Fig. 9) is on each side of the upper jaw and above and behind, but often parallel to the premaxillary. A splint-like supplementary maxillary may be applied to the upper edge of the maxillary. The posterior end of the maxillary usually marks the

11

end of the jaw, and its position in relation to the eye or orbit is often used in identification.

The lower jaw consists of several bones, the most important consisting of the *dentaries* which usually bear teeth. In a few primitive fishes, a prominent shield-like bone, the *gular plate* (Fig. 10), lies between the right and left jaws. The length of the lower jaw varies in different species; in some it may protrude beyond the upper jaw while in others it may be equal or may be shorter or *inferior*. The forward angle of the mandible forms the *chin*.

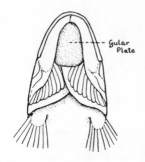

Figure 10

Almost any bone in the mouth of fishes is capable of bearing teeth. The roof is formed by an unpaired median *vomer* on each side of which are *palatines* extending to the pterygoids. In the floor of the mouth a bump formed by the protrusion of the *hyoid* bone and frequently bearing teeth, forms the *tongue*. The mouth when approximately at the anterior end of the head is said to be *terminal*. If the snout extends considerably before the mouth, the mouth is said to be *subterminal*.

The *barbels* are thread-like structures on the head especially around the mouth of many fishes. These are prominent on such fishes as catfishes, but may be small bumps at the end of the maxillary of some minnows (See Fig. 202).

The eye of the fish lies within the *orbit* (Fig. 9). The external diameter of the orbit or the distance from rim to rim is often used as a comparative measurement. Behind the eye, the *cheek* (Fig. 9) is the fleshy area extending to the edge of the *preopercle* which is marked by a groove. The bony *opercle* or gill cover lies back of the cheek and marks the posterior border of the head. The opercle consists of the thinly covered *opercular* bone below which are the subopercular and interopercular bones. The space under the eye and extending to the maxillary bone is the *suborbital* region.

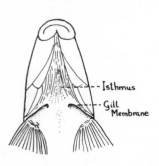

Figure 11

The *gill* or *branchiostegal membrane* (Fig. 9) is a thin membrane connecting the lower part of the opercle with the throat or with the opposite membrane. The membrane may form a close attachment with the throat or with the opposite membrane (Fig. 11), or it may extend far forward with a wide attachment leaving the anterior extension of the throat exposed as an *isthmus* (Fig.

12). The gill membrane is supported by a series of small slender bones known as the *branchiostegals* or *branchiostegal rays* (Fig. 9).

Under each opercle is the gill or *branchial chamber* containing usually 4 sets of gills. Each set of gills consist of a pair of bony, flesh-covered *pharyngeal arches* supporting a double row of red gill filaments. These are the actual respiratory structures of fishes. On the inner surface of the gill arch is a row of finger-like structures (may be filamentous in some) which are the *gill rakers* and may serve to prevent any objects from entering the gill chambers from the throat. Fishes obtain oxygen from the water which enters through the mouth and passes out over the gills.

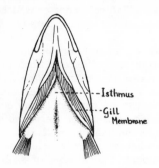

--Isthmus

--Gill Membrane

Figure 12

In some fishes a patch of rudimentary gill filaments known as *pseudobranchia* may appear on the inner surface of the opercular flap, representing a lost front gill. The fifth gill or pharyngeal arches become modified and no longer bear gills in many fishes, but may develop tooth-like structures known as *pharyngeal teeth* (See Fig. 32). These are very well-developed in suckers, minnows and other fishes which may not have teeth in their mouths. The arrangement and number of the pharyngeal teeth in the minnows is often an important character used in classification.

Fishes possess an external set of sensory structures known as the *lateral line* system. The most conspicuous part of this system appears as the *lateral line* (Fig. 2) commonly seen on the sides of the trunk and tail regions. A pattern of pores related to this system can sometimes be traced over the head. The lateral line consists of an external row of pores, one on each scale, which open into a canal imbedded under the skin. The sensory endings of a branch of the 10th cranial nerve lie in this canal. Many functions have been assigned to this system, but the most recent findings indicate that it functions in receiving vibrations from objects thus enabling the fish to swim blindly without hitting objects and also helping in capturing prey.

The size of various structures are important characters used in fish classification. Individual fishes vary so much in size that actual measurements are of little value, consequently, comparative ratios are generally used. Hence, the number of times the eye goes into the length of the snout or the number of times the body depth or the length of the head goes into the standard length is more significant than the actual measurement. *Depth of body* (Fig. 1) is the greatest depth of body measured in a straight line from dorsal to ventral surface at right angles to the length.

The length of a fish is often considered as a straight line measurement from the tip of the jaws or the tip of the snout, if the snout extends beyond the mouth to various posterior parts. Dividers should be used for all small fishes. *Total length* (Fig. 1) is the distance to the extreme tip of the caudal fin. *Fork length* is the distance to the fork of the caudal fin. *Body length* (Fig. 1) is to the base of the caudal fin. *Standard length* (Fig. 1) is the distance to the last vertebra which can be determined as approximately the flexure line or crease caused by bending the caudal fin. This is the measurement usually referred to in this book.

The number of scales on various parts of the body are useful aids in classification. The number is seldom constant but usually fluctuates within a definite range. *The number of scales in the lateral line* (Fig. 2) is an important measurement. Careful counting, often under magnification, is necessary. The pored scales can be counted to the end of the caudal vertebrae which can be determined as for the standard length. These counts usually vary within certain limits for each species. When the lateral line is incomplete or undeveloped, the number of vertical scale rows are commonly substituted. The number of scales in a row between the lateral line and the anterior base of the dorsal fin is designated as the scales above the *lateral line* (Fig. 2). Counts of the scales in a row from the lateral line to front of base of anal fin is known as the *scales below the lateral line* (Fig. 2). The number of mid-dorsal scales anterior to the dorsal fin, and the number of scale rows before the dorsal fin are frequently used in the identification of some species.

KEY TO THE FAMILIES OF FISHES FOUND IN THE FRESHWATERS OF THE UNITED STATES*

1a. Mouth without jaws and within a funnel-like depression lined with horny teeth; no paired fins; nostrils consist of an unpaired median pit; seven separate gill apertures on each side. Fig. 13........
...................LAMPREY FAMILY, Petromyzontidae, page 28

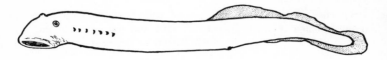

Figure 13

1b. Mouth with upper and lower jaws and not located in a funnel-like depression; nostrils consist of paired openings; one or two pairs of fins present; gills covered by a bony flap or opercle. Fig. 2 2

2a. Caudal fin is typical or modified hetero-cercal type. Figs. 3, 14..............3

2b. Caudal fin is homocercal type. Fig. 4..6

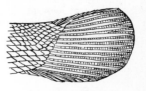

3a. Caudal fin is typically heterocercal (Fig. 3); mouth is under and behind tip of projecting snout (subterminal) and with no or with poorly developed teeth 4

Figure 14

3b. Caudal fin is modified heterocercal type (Fig. 14); mouth is located at tip of snout (terminal) and has well developed teeth.........5

4a. No scales or bony plates apparent on body; snout is very long and paddle-like; two tiny barbels in front of mouth. Fig. 15..........
..................PADDLEFISH FAMILY, Polyodontidae, page 37

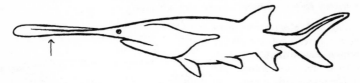

Figure 15

---

*Many families of marine fishes contain species which occasionally invade fresh and brackish waters at the mouths of rivers. Some, but not all, of these families are included here.

4b. Prominent bony plates on head; 5 rows of keeled plates on body; snout is shovel-like; 4 well developed barbels in front of mouth. Fig. 16.............STURGEON FAMILY, Acipenseridae, page 34

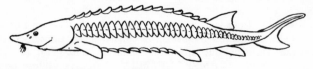

Figure 16

5a. Jaws very elongated; body covered with hard diamond-shape or ganoid scales (Fig. 6); dorsal fin short and near caudal fin. Fig. 17........................GAR FAMILY, Lepisosteidae, page 39

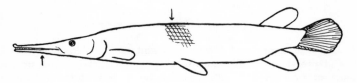

Figure 17

5b. Jaws not elongated; body covered with cycloid scales (Fig. 7); dorsal fin very long, extending over most of the back and almost to the caudal fin. Fig. 18....BOWFIN FAMILY, Amiidae, page 38

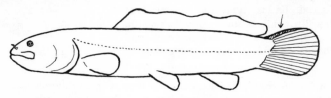

Figure 18

6a. Pelvic fins absent; body elongated or eel-like................7

6b. Pelvic fins usually present (absent in a few cavefishes and some western desert fishes); body not eel-like........................8

7a. Snout not elongated; body covered with minute scales which are difficult to see; dorsal fin elongated and continuous with caudal fin. Fig. 19 .... FRESHWATER EEL FAMI-LY, Anguillidae, page 155

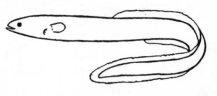

Figure 19

7b. Snout elongated with small mouth at tip; body covered with an-
nular rings or plates; dorsal fin small and not reaching caudal fin.
Fig. 20............PIPEFISH FAMILY, Syngnathidae, page 159
Marine, but occasionally enter freshwater.

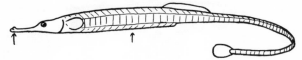

Figure 20

8a. Pelvic fins near anus, abdominal in position. Fig. 21.....9

8b. Pelvic fins near, under, or in
front of pectoral fins, thoracic
or jugular in position. Fig. 22.
.........................29

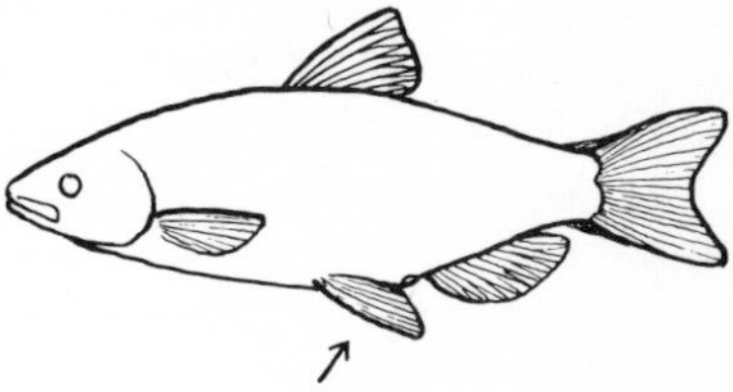

9a. Head without scales.......10

9b. Head more or less covered
with scales 22

Figure 21

10a. Fins usually without spines;
spines present only in fins of
introduced minnows (carp
and goldfish) and some desert minnows from southwestern U. S. 11

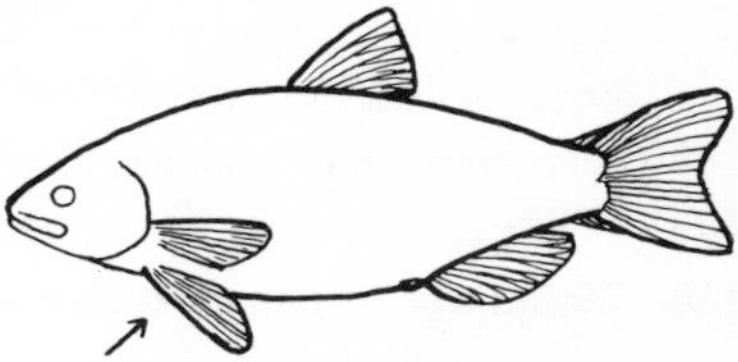

Figure 22

10b. Fins with both spines and soft rays........................21

11a. Four or more branchiostegal rays present on each side.......12

11b. Less than four branchiostegal rays present on each side......19

12a. No adipose fin present...................................13

12b. Adipose fin present. Fig. 2...............................17

13a. Belly with rounded and smooth margin....................14

13b. Belly with saw-tooth or with a knife-like margin............15

14a. Last ray of dorsal fin not elongated. Fig. 23.................
..................TEN POUNDER FAMILY, Elopidae, page 41
Marine sometimes enter freshwater.

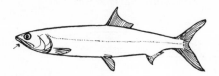

Figure 23

14b. Last ray of dorsal fin greatly elongated. Fig. 24. ....TARPON FAMILY, Megalopidae, page 41

Marine   sometimes   enter freshwater.

Figure 24

15a. Mouth very large with maxillary extend i n g behind posterior margin of eye. Fig. 25. ANCHOVY FAMILY, Engraulidae, page 45

Marine sometimes enter freshwater.

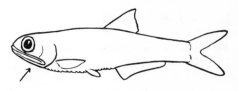

Figure 25

15b. Mouth not large; maxillary does not reach past the eye......16

16a. Lateral line absent; belly with saw-tooth margin entire length. Fig. 26......HERRING F A M I L Y, Clupeidae, page 42

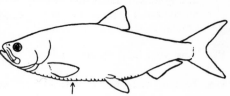

Figure 26

16b. Lateral line present; part of belly with sharp but not saw-tooth margin. Fig. 27. MOONEYE FAMILY, Hiodontidae, page 44

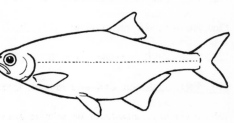

Figure 27

17a. No axillary process at base of pelvic fin. Fig. 28 . . . .
. . . . SMELT FAMILY, Osmeridae, page 58

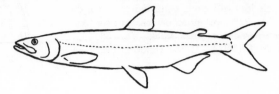

Figure 28

17b. Axillary process present at base of pelvic fin 18

18a. Dorsal fin as long or longer than head and with more than 15
rays. Fig. 29 . . . . GRAYLING FAMILY, Thymallidae, page 57

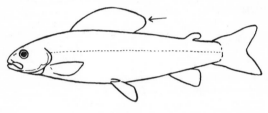

Figure 29

18b. Dorsal fin shorter than head and with less than 15 rays. Fig. 30.
. . . . SALMON FAMILY, Salmonidae, page 46

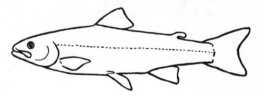

Figure 30

19a. Adipose fin present;
teeth are present in
mouth. Fig. 31 . . . . . .
CHARACIN FAMILY,
Characidae, page 64 →

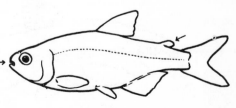

19b. Adipose fin absent;
no teeth present in
mouth 20

Figure 31

20a. Usually more than 10 dorsal rays; (some *Pantosteus* have 9-10 dorsal rays) more than 10 well developed pharyngeal teeth on each last gill arch confined to a single row (Fig. 32); lips more or less sucker-like, lower lip more or less thick. Fig. 33.....
SUCKER FAMILY, Catostomidae, page 64

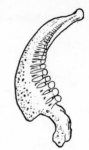

Figure 32

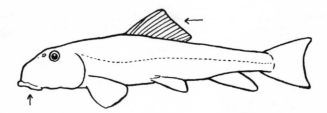

Figure 33

20b. Usually not more than 10 dorsal rays (except in introduced carp, goldfish, and in several western minnows); less than 10 pharyngeal teeth on each last gill arch confined to 2 or 3 rows; or if in a single row, only 4-5 teeth on each side (Fig. 34); lips usually not sucker-like. Fig. 35.....
..MINNOW FAMILY, Cyprinidae, page 79

Figure 34

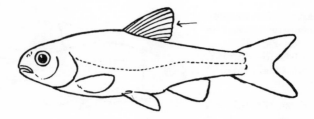

Figure 35

21a. Conspicuous barbels present above and below mouth; body without scales. Fig. 36....CATFISH FAMILY, Ictaluridae, page 147

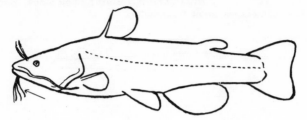

Figure 36

21b. Barbels absent above and below mouth; body scaled. Fig. 37. TROUTPERCH FAMILY, Percopsidae, page 177

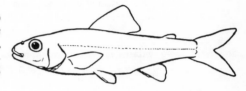

Figure 37

22a. Small spiny dorsal fin in front of soft dorsal fin............23
22b. No spiny dorsal fin in front of soft dorsal fin................24
23a. Lower jaw more or less extending before upper jaw, snout flattened; eye not partly covered by adipose membrane. Fig. 38.
...................SILVERSIDES FAMILY, Atherinidae, page 180

Figure 38

23b. Lower jaw does not extend beyond upper jaw; eye partly covered by vertical adipose membrane. Fig. 39................
........................MULLET FAMILY, Mugilidae, page 179
Marine sometimes enter freshwater.

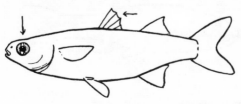

Figure 39

21

24a. Lateral line ventral in position; about 300 scales in lateral line; jaws very long and slender. Fig. 40.........................
..................NEEDLEFISH FAMILY, Belonidae, page 156
Marine sometimes enter freshwater.

Figure 40

24b. Lateral line imperfect or absent; dorsal in position when present; jaws variable, but not slender; less than 200 scales in lateral line 25

25a. Both jaws extend forward and shaped like a duck bill. Fig. 41.
...........................PIKE FAMILY, Esocidae, page 61

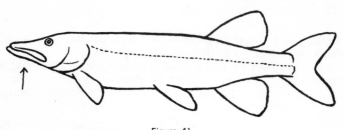

Figure 41

25b. Both jaws not extending far forward and not shaped like a duck bill 26

26a. Lower jaw not protruding. Fig. 42..........................
....................MUDMINNOW FAMILY, Umbridae, page 60

Figure 42

26b. Lower jaw protruding.......................................27

27a. Eyes degenerate or small; pelvic fins minute or absent; anus tends to be jugular. Fig. 43..................................
..................CAVEFISH FAMILY, Amblyopsidae, page 160

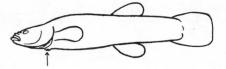

Figure 43

27b. Eyes normal; pelvic fins usually well developed (except in a few desert species) 28

28a. Third anal ray (including rudimentary rays) not branched (Fig. 44); anal fin of male modified into elongated intromittent organ (goniopodium). Fig. 45. ....TOPMINNOW or LIVE-BEARER FAMILY, Poeciliidae, page 175

Figure 44

Figure 45

28b. Third anal ray branched; may not be completely divided in immature individuals; in some the second ray is also branched; anal fin of male not modified. Fig. 46....... ....KILLI-FISH FAMILY, Cyprinodontidae page 161

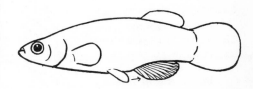

Figure 46

23

29a. Fins without spines or hard rays............................30
29b. Fins with spines or hard rays................................33
30a. Both eyes on one side of head; body compressed laterally and fish lives on its side; (FLATFISHES, marine, but some species are frequent invaders of freshwater)........................31
30b. Eyes normal; body not compressed laterally; median barbel under chin. Fig. 47..............COD FAMILY, Gadidae, page 156

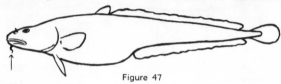

Figure 47

31a. Margin of preopercle hidden by skin; left pectoral fin rudimentary or absent, right pectoral fin may or may not be present. Fig. 48..SOLE FAMILY, Achiridae, page 238 Marine sometimes enter freshwater.

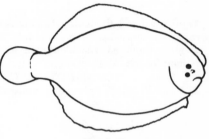

Figure 48

31b. Margin of preopercle not obscured by skin; both pectoral fins present.....32
32a. Pelvic fins not symmetrical but fin on eyed side located on ventral margin. Fig. 49 .... FLATFISH FAMILY, Bothidae, page 237
Marine sometimes enter freshwater.

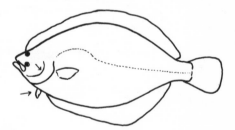

Figure 49

32b. Pelvic fins symmetrical, no fin on ventral margin. Fig. 50 ....FLOUNDER FAMILY, Pleuronectidae page 238
Marine sometimes enter freshwater.

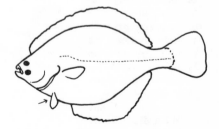

Figure 50

33a. **Adults with anus anterior to usual position, usually under throat (jugular). Fig. 51...** ....PIRATEPERCH FAMILY, Aphredoderidae, page 178

Figure 51

33b. **Adults with anus in normal position........................34**

34a. **Body without scales, naked or covered with tiny spines or with plates 35**

34b. **Body with scales...36**

35a. **Free spines in front of soft dorsal fin; pelvic fin formed of one spine. Fig. 52..STICKLEBACK FAMILY, Gasterosteidae, page 157**

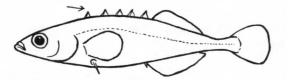

Figure 52

35b. **Dorsal spines not free but united to each other by fin membrane; pelvic fins with 3 or 4 soft rays; pectoral fins very large. Fig. 53 .... SCULPIN FAMILY, Cottidae, page 231**

Figure 53

36a. **Dorsal fin with 16 or more spines.........................37**

36b. **Dorsal fin with less than 16 spines.......................38**

37a. Distinct r i d g e of scales along base of dorsal fin; lateral line complete. Fig. 54 ....SURF-FISH FAMILY, Embiotocidae, page 229

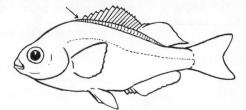

Figure 54

37b. No distinct ridge of scales at base of dorsal fin; lateral line broken under posterior part of dorsal fin. Fig. 55.... ..CICHLID FAMILY, Cichlidae, page 228

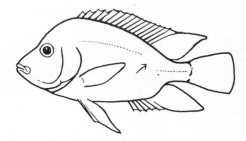

Figure 55

38a. Dorsal fin with 6 to 8 rather filamentous spines; pelvic fins sometimes united 39

38b. Dorsal fin with 4 to 15 rather stiff spines; pelvic fins never united. 40

39a. Pelvic fins close together and united. Fig. 56................... ....GOBY FAMILY, Gobiidae, page 230 Mostly marine. Sometimes enter freshwater.

Figure 56

39b. Pelvic fins not united. Fig.
57 ....SLEEPER
FAMILY, Eleotridae, page
229

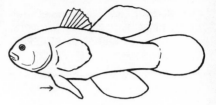

Figure 57

40a. Dorsal fin with 4 spines; pectoral fins on upper half of body.
(See Fig. 39)...........MULLET FAMILY, Mugilidae, page 179
40b. Dorsal fin with 6 to 15 spines; pectoral fins on lower half of body.
....41
41a. Anal spines 3 or more....................................42
41b. Anal spines less than 3..................................43
42a. Opercles with well developed spine; well developed patch of
gill filaments (pseudobranchia) on inner surface of opercle. Fig. 58.
...........................BASS FAMILY, Serranidae, page 181

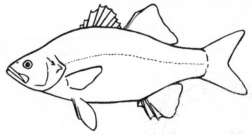

Figure 58

42b. Opercles without a well developed spine; poorly developed and
partly concealed vestigial gill filaments (pseudobranchia) on the
inner surface of the opercle. Fig. 59.........................
...................SUNFISH FAMILY, Centrarchidae, page 183

Figure 59

27

43a. Second anal spine broad and long; lateral line extends onto the caudal fin. Fig. 60. . . . .
. . . . DRUM or SHEEPHEAD FAMILY, Sciaenidae, page 227

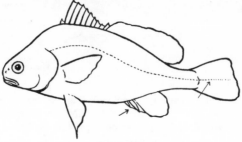

Figure 60

43b. Second anal spine not very broad and long; lateral line not extending onto caudal fin. Fig. 61. . . . .
. . . . PERCH FAMILY, Percidae, page 196

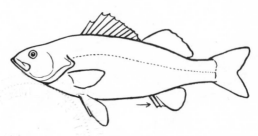

Figure 61

LAMPREY FAMILY, Petromyzontidae

The members of the lamprey family are eel-like forms with a sucker-disc mouth structure (buccal funnel) filled with horny spines called teeth. The lampreys are highly specialized descendants of the earliest known type of vertebrates and have never possessed upper and lower jaws, true teeth, and paired fins. Their skeleton is very primitive, consisting chiefly of an incomplete cartilaginous brain case and a notochord on top of which are vestiges of vertebrae. No true bone is present. The gills are highly specialized and lie in separate pockets represented by seven clefts on each side of the body. They possess a long dorsal fin which is more or less continuous with the caudal fin. Lampreys vary in size from six inches to several feet. Most of the freshwater species are pale brown or fawn color.

Adult lampreys are modified for a parasitic life, possessing a sucker-disc by which they can attach to fishes and rasp a hole for gorging on the blood. The funnel is lined with cornified spines called teeth. The adults of some species have abandoned this mode of feeding, and do not feed after metamorphosis, but live just long enough in the adult stage to reproduce. These have smaller buccal funnels and feeble teeth.

The lampreys deposit their eggs in nests made on the bottom of swift streams by pulling back the pebbles. The eggs hatch into larval forms known as *ammocoetes*. These have undeveloped eyes and no sucking disc. The larval forms spend approximately 4 to 5 years in the bottom mud of streams where they feed on organic detritus, eventually metamorphosing into adults with eyes and sucker-discs (buccal funnels).

Several species live in the sea and enter freshwater to spawn. These may become landlocked and develop freshwater races. Other species are entirely freshwater and are found in most of the river systems and lakes of the United States.

1a. Dorsal fin separated into 2 parts...2

1b. Dorsal fin continuous (Genus *Ichthyomyzon*) 7

Figure 62

2a. More than 3 radiating rows of teeth, 4 or more teeth in each row on each side of opening in buccal funnel (Fig. 62); may reach a length of 2 feet. Fig. 63......................**SEA LAMPREY,** *Petromyzon marinus* Linnaeus.

Brownish and strongly mottled. Anadromous on the Atlantic coast. The landlocked form, *Petromyzon marinus dorsatus* Wilder, is a dwarfed form found in some eastern lakes and is a recent invader of the Great Lakes.

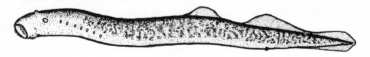

Figure 63

2b. Scattered groups of teeth not in radiating rows, usually 3 groups of one or two large teeth on each side of opening in buccal funnel 3

29

3a. Upper tooth (supraoral) plate with three well developed teeth (plate with large teeth above opening in buccal funnel, Fig. 64); dorsal fin separated by wide space; may reach a length of 2 feet. Fig. 65 ....PA-CIFIC or THREE-TOOTHED LAMPREY, *Entosphenus tridentatus* (Gairdner).

Figure 64

Anadromous in streams of Pacific coast from southern California northward.

Figure 65

3b. Tooth (supraoral) plate above opening in buccal funnel with no central tooth, usually with 2 or more less developed teeth; dorsal fins separated by an acute or sharp notch except in *L. fluviatilis*..4

Figure 66

4a. Dorsal fin separated by a wide notch or interspace; teeth well developed (Fig. 66); usually 8 to 12 inches in length. Fig. 67....
..................RIVER LAMPREY, *Lampetra aryresii* (Gunther)
Anadromous in streams of Pacific coast.

Figure 67

4b. Dorsal fin separated by rather sharp or acute notch; teeth poorly developed and very minute; non-parasitic..........5

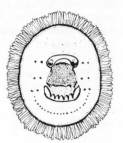

Figure 68

5a. Found in streams west of the Rockies; no large lateral teeth (Fig. 68); usually 7 to 9 inches in length. Fig. 69......
.....................WESTERN BROOK LAMPREY, *Lampetra planeri* Bloch.

Very similar if not the same as the eastern brook lamprey. Small lamprey in streams of Pacific coast and northern Asia.

Figure 69

5b. Found in streams east of Rockies; 3 or more well-developed lateral teeth 6

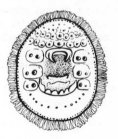

Figure 70

6a. Segments (myomeres) between last gill cleft and anus over 60; about 6 to 8 inches long. Figs. 70, 71.............
.....................EASTERN BROOK LAMPREY, *Lampetra lamottei* (LeSueur).

Small lamprey common in small streams northward from Missouri, Tennessee, and from Maryland to Connecticut.

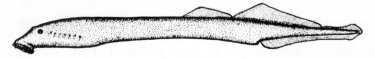

Figure 71

6b. Segments (myomeres) between last gill cleft and anus less than 60; teeth very minute; teeth in upper tooth band (supra-oral) consist of a pair of bicuspid tubercles (Fig. 72); usually 6 to 8 inches long. Fig. 73...................OHIO BROOK LAMPREY, *Lampetra aepyptera* Abbott

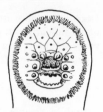

Resembles eastern brook lamprey. Small streams of upper Ohio drainage and from Potomac to Neuse Rivers and in some Gulf coastal streams.

Figure 72

Figure 73

7a. Parasitic; diameter of buccal funnel larger than width of head...8

7b. Non-parasitic; diameter of buccal funnel not larger than width of head 10

8a. Teeth on each side of oral opening in buccal funnel (circumoral teeth) mostly unicuspid or with one point (Fig. 74); may reach a length of 15 inches. Fig. 75.........SILVER LAMPREY, *Ichthyo-myzon unicuspis* Hubbs and Trautman

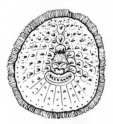

In upper Mississippi drainage and in parts of Hudson Bay and Great Lakes drainages.

Figure 74

Figure 75

8b. Teeth on each side of oral opening in buccal funnel (circumoral teeth) mostly bicuspid or with 2 points........................9

9a. Segments or myomeres between last gill cleft and anus usually 51 to 54; may reach a length of 15 inches.....
......CHESTNUT LAMPREY, *Ichthyomyzon castaneus* Hubbs and Trautman

Resembles silver lamprey but differs in having well developed bicuspid teeth on each side of buccal funnel (Fig. 76). Northern Wisconsin to Louisiana and Alabama, also in western Manitoba and in parts of Great Lakes drainage.

Figure 76

9b. Segments or myomeres between last gill cleft and anus usually 56 to 58; may reach a length of 12 inches (See Fig. 75)...........
.................OHIO LAMPREY, *Ichthyomyzon bdellium* Jordan
Resembles silver lamprey. Ohio River system.

10a. Teeth small and poorly developed; circumoral teeth (teeth on each side of opening in buccal funnel) not with double points (bicuspid) (Fig. 77); may reach a length of 10 inches. Fig. 78.. NORTHERN BROOK LAMPREY, *Ichthyomyzon fossor* Reighard and Cummins

Wisconsin eastward in Great Lakes drainage.

Figure 77

Figure 78

10b. Teeth moderately to well-developed; circumoral teeth with double points (bicuspid) 11

11a. Segments or myomeres between last gill cleft and anus 51 to 54; may reach a length of 9 inches.......................SOUTHERN BROOK LAMPREY, *Ichthyomyzon gagei* Hubbs and Trautman
Resembles northern brook lamprey. Lower Mississippi drainage.

11b. Segments or myomeres between last gill cleft and anus 55 to 61;
may reach a length of 12 inches..................ALLEGHENY
BROOK LAMPREY, *Ichthyomyzon greeleyi* Hubbs and Trautman
Resembles northern brook lamprey. Upper Ohio River drainage.

A closely related species, *Ichthyomyzon hubbsi* Raney, in the upper
Tennessee River drainage closely resembles the Allegheny brook lamprey but differs in having weaker teeth and a much lower first dorsal fin.

STURGEON FAMILY, Acipenseridae

The sturgeons are modern relicts of some of the early bony fishes.
Many of their structures are quite primitive, indicating that they are
survivors of an ancient group. They possess a primitive heterocercal
caudal fin and a spiral valve intestine. Their skeleton is largely cartilaginous and they retain a notochord. Bony plates cover their heads
and extend in several longitudinal rows along their bodies. Scales
are mostly restricted to a patch of ganoid scales on the caudal fin.

Sturgeons possess a more or less prolonged shovel-shape snout
under which is a sucker-like mouth with thick lips. The mouth is well
adapted for working over the bottom where they pick up small animals
for food. A row of sensory barbels before the mouth aids in locating
their food.

Sturgeons occur in Northern Europe, Asia and North America. Some
attain huge size, some in Russia having been reported as weighing
over a ton. Many species are anadromous, living in the sea and entering freshwater to spawn. The three species found in the central United
States are strictly freshwater, but those found on the west and east
coasts are anadromous.

Sturgeons spawn in the spring, passing upstream to gravel beds
where they deposit their eggs. They give no care to the eggs or
young. Sturgeons are quite important as the flesh is excellent for food
and the eggs are used for caviar.

1a. Small opening (spiracle) between eye and upper corner of opercle
(Fig. 79); caudal peduncle heavy and not entirely covered by bony
plates; lower lip with 2 slightly papillose lobes, none on upper
lip, (Fig. 80), (*Acipenser*)......................................3

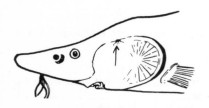

Figure 79

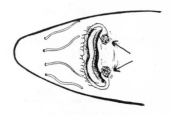

Figure 80

1b. No opening (spiracle) between eye and upper corner of opercle (Fig. 81); caudal peduncle very slender and completely enclosed by plates; lower lip with 4 papillose lobes, (Fig. 82), (*Scaphirhynchus*) 2

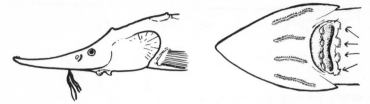

Figure 81   Figure 82

2a. Belly covered with small bony scale-like plates. Fig. 83....SHOV-ELNOSE STURGEON, *Scaphirhynchus platorynchus* (Rafinesque)
Pale brown. Length about 2 feet, although records of 5 feet are reported. Mississippi River and larger tributaries.

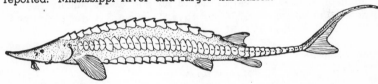

Figure 83

2b. Belly mostly naked.......................................PAL-LID STURGEON, *Scaphirhynchus album* (Forbes and Richardson)
Light brown. Length about 2 feet, although may reach a length of nearly 5 feet. Rare, in upper Mississippi River and larger tributaries.

3a. Bony plates between pelvic and anal fins in 2 rows of 4 to 8 each (Fig. 84), dorsal rays about 45. Fig. 85......WHITE STURGEON, *Acipenser transmontanus* Richardson

Grayish brown. Reaches large size of over 8 feet. Anadromous, Pacific coast from Monterey northward.

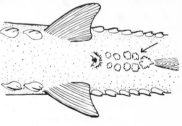

Figure 84

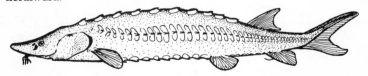

Figure 85

3b. Bony plates between pelvic and anal fins in one row of 1 to 4 plates (Fig. 86); dorsal rays less than 45.........................4

4a. Space between dorsal and lateral rows of plates containing 4 to 10 rows of smaller star-shape plates 5

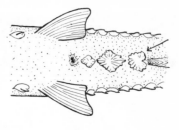

Figure 86

4b. Space between dorsal and lateral rows of plates containing many rows of minute plates or spicules 6

5a. Anal fin almost as long as dorsal fin and about entirely behind dorsal fin; dorsal rays 33; anal rays 22; about 9 dorsal plates and 26 lateral plates. Fig. 87......................................
................GREEN STURGEON, *Acipenser medirostris* Ayres
Greenish color. Size small. Snout more pointed than that of other Pacific species, *A. transmontanus.*
Anadromous, Pacific coast from San Francisco northward.

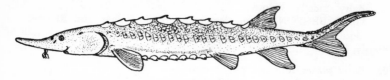

Figure 87

5b. Anal fin not much more than 1/2 as long as dorsal fin and almost entirely below it; dorsal rays 38; anal rays 27; about 10 dorsal plates and 29 lateral plates. Fig. 88.........................
.........ATLANTIC STURGEON, *Acipenser oxyrhynchus* Mitchill
Olive gray or brown reaching a length of 12 feet.
Anadromous, Atlantic coast North Carolina into New England.

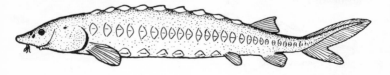

Figure 88

6a. Front of anal fin below front of dorsal fin and 1/2 as long as dorsal fin; dorsal rays about 41; anal rays about 22; about 8-11 dorsal plates and 22-33 lateral plates. Fig. 89........................
........SHORTNOSE STURGEON, *Acipenser brevirostris* LeSueur

Length not much over 2 feet. Anadromous, Atlantic coast from Florida to Cape Cod.

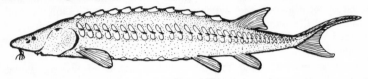

Figure 89

6b. Front of anal fin below middle of dorsal fin and about 2/3 as long as dorsal fin; dorsal rays 35-39; anal rays 22-28; about 15 dorsal plates and 30 to 38 lateral plates. Fig. 90........................
.............LAKE STURGEON, *Acipenser fulvescens* Rafinesque

Brownish sometimes mottled. Lengths of over 7 feet are known. Freshwater, Great Lakes, and Upper Mississippi drainages, and in the Saskatchewan and Hudson Bay drainages.

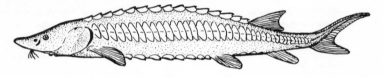

Figure 90

PADDLEFISH FAMILY, Polyodontidae

The paddlefish family contains only one American species, the PADDLEFISH, *Polyodon spathula* (Walbaum) (Fig. 91) found in the larger streams and connected waters of the Mississippi drainage. Another species, *Psephurus gladius* is found in China. These represent relicts of an ancient and primitive group. They possess a hetero-

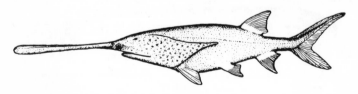

Figure 91

cercal caudal fin and a spiral valve intestine. The internal skeleton is mostly cartilage.

The paddlefish is characterized by a long flat snout resembling a paddle. The body is covered by smooth skin and the only evidence of scales is a small patch of ganoid scales on the caudal fin. The gills are covered by opercles with long pointed flaps reaching far back on the body. The gill rakers are filamentous and form a very efficient sieve for straining out the food. These fishes swim about with their mouths open, allowing the water to pass in and out through the gills straining out the plankton crustacea and other small animals on which they feed. They reach a length of over eight feet and a weight of over 200 pounds.

Little is known about the reproductive habits of the paddlefish. The young are hatched without a paddle-snout, and this structure develops as the fish grows. They are an excellent food fish, and their eggs are sometimes used for caviar.

BOWFIN FAMILY, Amiidae

The bowfin family contains but one living species known as the BOWFIN or FRESHWATER DOGFISH, *Amia calva* Linnaeus, (Fig. 92), which is generally recognized as a survivor of an early primitive group. They retain much cartilage in their skeleton and have a sheath of bony plates covering their semi-cartilaginous skull. Under the throat a bony plate, known as the gular plate, fills the space between the lower jaws. The young are hatched with a heterocercal caudal fin which changes with growth into a modified heterocercal type. The body is covered by cycloid scales.

This fish is readily identified by its long dorsal fin reaching almost to the caudal fin. Bowfins are olive green on the back, shading lighter on the sides to yellow on the belly. Their backs and sides are more or less mottled. The males have an ocellus or "eye spot" at the base of the caudal fin. The lower fins become a vivid blue-green during the breeding season. Bowfins retain a connection between the swim bladder and the pharynx which enables them to use the swim bladder as a respiratory organ. They rise frequently to the surface and take

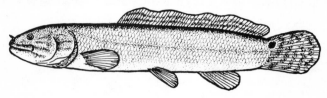

Figure 92

a fresh "breath" which enables them to live in stagnant waters where the oxygen may be insufficient for most other fishes.

Bowfins spawn in the spring. The male clears out a bowl-like depression in shallow water and guards the eggs and newly hatched fry for several weeks. Bowfins feed on all sorts of living animals, preying heavily on small fishes. Their flesh is not very palatable, and they are seldom used for food. They reach a length of over 2 feet and a weight of ten pounds.

Bowfins occur in sluggish rivers and shallow lakes of the Mississippi drainage from Minnesota eastward through part of the Great Lakes and St. Lawrence drainages and south to the Gulf. They range southward in the Atlantic drainage from Connecticut to Florida.

GAR FAMILY, Lepisosteidae

The gar family contains about 10 species which are restricted to Central and, North America and the West Indies. The gars are primitive fishes, retaining much cartilage in their skeleton. Their heads are covered with bony plates. They are characterized by a long cylindrical body covered with ganoid scales and by long jaws heavily armed with sharp teeth.

Five species of gars are found in the United States east of the Rockies. These inhabit warm sluggish waters where they lie in wait for their prey. They feed on all kinds of fishes both dead and alive. They have a swim bladder which retains a wide passage to the pharynx, and they use this organ for part of their respiration. Hence, they can live in very stagnant waters. They spawn in the spring depositing their eggs at random in shallow water, giving no care to the eggs or young. The eggs are quite toxic and cause great distress if eaten.

1a. Distance from tip of snout to angle of jaw slightly shorter than rest of head (Fig. 93); mouth of adults with 2 rows of large teeth in upper jaw; snout broad and blunt Fig. 94.... .... ALLI-GATOR GAR, *Lepisosteus spatula* Lacépède

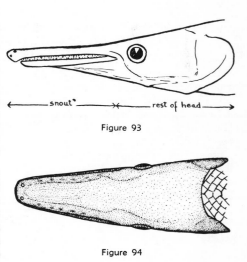

Figure 93

Figure 94

Greenish or olivaceous above, pale below; snout broader than in shortnose gar. Reaches a very large size of over 12 feet in length. Gulf drainage and Mississippi River north to St. Louis.

1b. Distance from tip of snout to angle of jaw as long or longer than rest of head. Mouth with 1 row of large teeth (teeth of inner row mostly small) in upper jaw....................................2

2a. Snout long and slender, length more than twice the distance from angle of mouth to posterior edge of opercle. Fig. 95.............
...............LONGNOSE GAR, *Lepisosteus osseus* (Linnaeus)
Olivaceous above and silvery below; a few large spots on body posteriorly. Length up to 5 feet. Minnesota to Vermont and south to Gulf and Rio Grande River.

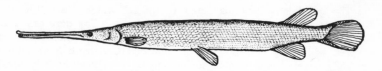

Figure 95

2b. Snout short and broad. Length less than twice the distance from the angle of the mouth to the posterior edge of the opercle. Fig. 96 3

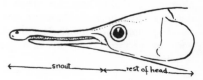

Figure 96

3a. Top of head with large round spots; diffuse spots on fins; 54 to 58 scale rows along side of body. Figs. 97, 98....................
....................SPOTTED GAR, *Lepisosteus productus* Cope

Olivaceous above and silvery below; large spots scattered on body posteriorly. Length up to 4 feet. Iowa and Nebraska to Gulf. A closely allied species, the FLORIDA GAR, *Lepisosteus platyrhincus* DeKay replaces this form in Florida and southern Georgia. It differs in having a broader and shorter snout.

Length up to 30 inches.

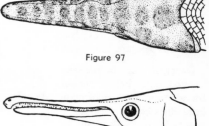

Figure 97

Figure 98

40

3b. Top of head without spots (Fig. 99); small well-defined spots on fins; 60 to 64 scale rows along side of body. Fig. 100 . . . .
. . . . SHORTNOSE GAR, *Lepisosteus platostomus* Rafinesque

Olivaceous above and silvery below; large spots on body posteriorly. Length of 3-4 feet. Great Lakes and Mississippi Valley to northeastern Texas.

Figure 99

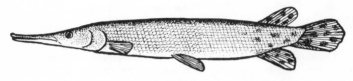

Figure 100

TEN POUNDER FAMILY, Elopidae

The members of this family live in the sea, but several species may invade a short distance into freshwater. The TEN POUNDER or BIG EYE HERRING, *Elops saurus* Linnaeus (Fig. 101) often enters rivers in the Gulf States, and a similar species may also enter freshwater in California. These fish are silvery and possess a gular plate between the lower jaws similar to that in *Amia calva*. The eyes are covered by adipose eyelids. They possess pseudobranchiae and long slender gill rakers. The dorsal and anal fins are depressible into a sheath of scales. The ten pounder reaches a length of 3 feet.

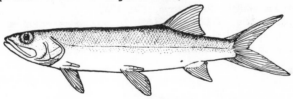

Figure 101

TARPON FAMILY, Megalopidae

This is a marine family closely related to the Elopidae, but differing in the lack of pseudobranchiae and in several internal structures. This family is represented by the TARPON, *Megalops atlantica* Valenciennes, which is one of the best known game fishes of the southern Atlantic and Gulf of Mexico. The tarpon (Fig. 102) often enters freshwater streams of Florida and other Gulf States. It has a gular plate and is characterized by large silverish scales and a long filamentous posterior ray in the dorsal fin. It reaches a length of over 6 feet but those caught in freshwater are usually much smaller.

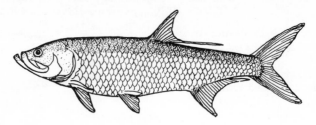

Figure 102

HERRING FAMILY, Clupeidae

The herring family contains many important marine species including the true herring. Several species are common in freshwater, including some anadromous species living in the sea, but entering freshwater to spawn.

Members of this family are characterized by having a saw-toothed edge on the belly. They are thin fishes with silvery scales and bluish backs. Many have one or more spots on sides. Some of the anadromous species have spectacular spawning runs in the spring as they crowd upstream to spawn. No care is given to the eggs or young. They feed on a variety of small animal life. Some, such as the gizzard shad, strain out and utilize the larger plankton crustacea. Many species are utilized for food, and all are valuable forage fishes.

1a. Last ray of dorsal fin greatly elongated, forming a long filament. .2

1b. Last ray of dorsal fin not elongated.........................3

2a. Anal fin with 30 to 33 rays. Fig. 103...........................
...............GIZZARD SHAD, *Dorosoma cepedianum* (LeSueur)

Length up to 18 inches. Commonly found in freshwater, but may enter brackish water. Minnesota to St. Lawrence River and New Jersey, south to Gulf and into Mexico.

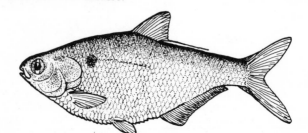

Figure 103

2b. **Anal fin with 20 to 25 rays**......................................
..............**THREADFIN SHAD,** *Dorosoma petenense* **(Gunther)**
Similar to gizzard shad. Length 8-10 inches. Gulf of Mexico, entering streams from Florida into Mexico.

3a. **Teeth present on rim (premaxillaries) of upper jaw; gill rakers short. Fig. 104..RIVER HERRING,** *Alosa chrysochloris* **(Rafinesque)**
Bluish above and silvery below. Length up to 15 inches. Gulf of Mexico, entering various river systems including the Mississippi river where it extends upstream to Minnesota.

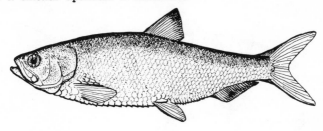

Figure 104

OHIO SHAD, *Alosa ohiensis* Evermann. Resembles river herring. Lower jaw about equal to length of upper which bears a central notch. Formerly in the Ohio River and parts of the Mississippi River, but has been considered extinct. However, it was recently reported from Oklahoma by Dr. George Moore.

3b. **Teeth more or less restricted to tongue and vomer, absent on rim (premaxillaries) of upper jaw; gill rakers long**..................**4**

4a. **Silvery patch on cheek deeper than long; more than 55 gill rakers on lower part of first gill arch. Fig. 105**..........................
..................**AMERICAN SHAD,** *Alosa sapidissima* **(Wilson)**
Bluish above and silvery white below; one or more spots in a longitudinal row behind opercle. Length up to 30 inches. Anadromous, Atlantic coast, entering rivers to spawn. Introduced and now abundant on Pacific coast.

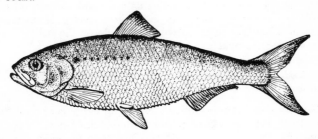

Figure 105

ALABAMA SHAD, *Alosa alabamae* Jordan and Evermann. Resembles the American shad. Anadromous in the Suwannee, Apalachicola, and Alabama River systems.

4b. Silvery patch on cheek longer than deep; less than 55 gill rakers on lower part of first gill arch. Fig. 106......................
........................ALEWIFE, *Alosa pseudoharengus* (Wilson)
Bluish above and silvery below; a dark spot behind opercle. Length 15 inches. Anadromous along Atlantic coast and often landlocked. Recently entered the Great Lakes.

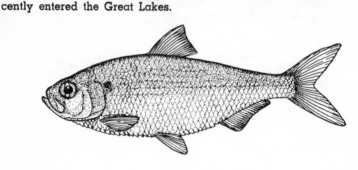

Figure 106

HICKORY SHAD or FALLHERRING, *A. mediocris* (Mitchill). Similar to alewife. Atlantic Ocean from Cape Cod to Florida, sometimes entering freshwater.

GLUT HERRING, *Alosa aestivalis* (Mitchill). Very similar to the alewife, but is more slender and has a dark peritoneum. Anadromous, ranging from Bay of Fundy to Florida. Length 12 inches.
Several species of menhaden, similar to the American shad, but readily recognized by their fluted scales, are common along the Atlantic and Gulf coasts and may enter mouths of rivers.

MOONEYE FAMILY, Hiodontidae

The family Hiodontidae contains only several species, all of which are strictly freshwater. They are thinbodied, silvery fishes resembling the herrings, but lacking the saw-tooth margin on the belly. The heads are small, and the eyes are large.

They feed on small aquatic organisms, including small fishes. They are utilized to a limited extent for food, mostly as smoked goldeye in the north.

1a. Belly keeled anterior to pelvic fins; front margins of anal fin about under or even with front margin of dorsal fin; 9 dorsal rays usually present. Fig. 107........GOLDEYE, *Hiodon alosoides* (Rafinesque)

Silvery somewhat darker on back. Length over 15 inches. Saskatchewan and Hudson Bay drainage south to Ohio drainage in Tennessee.

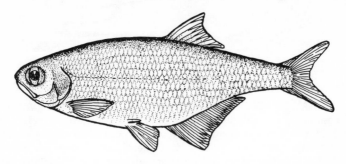

Figure 107

1b. Belly keeled between pelvic and anal fins; front margin of anal fin is below center of dorsal fin; 11 to 12 dorsal rays present. Fig. 108......................MOONEYE, *Hiodon tergisus* LeSueur
Silvery with somewhat dusky shades along back. Length 15 inches. Saskatchewan to St. Lawrence and Lake Champlain drainage.

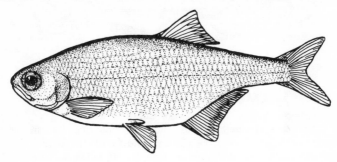

Figure 108

SOUTHERN MOONEYE, *Hiodon selenops* Jordan and Bean. Resembles the mooneye, but lacks a keel on the belly margin. Tennessee and Cumberland Rivers and from the lower Mississippi drainage.

ANCHOVY FAMILY, Engraulidae

The anchovy family contains small elongated fishes with rather compressed bodies, found in the warmer seas. They are closely allied to the herring family. Several species may enter freshwater.

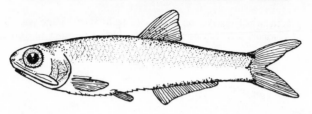

Figure 109

The BAY or MITCHILLS ANCHOVY, *Anchoa mitchilli* (Valenciennes) commonly invades freshwaters from Massachusetts to Texas. This is a small fish 2 to 4 inches in length with a pale silvery body peppered with tiny black spots and with a faint lateral band. This fish (Fig. 109) is easily distinguished by its large mouth and long maxillary which extends far back of the posterior margin of the orbit. The STRIPED ANCHOVY, *Anchoa hepsetus* (Linnaeus) (Fig. 110) with fewer anal rays (18 to 23) is common along the coast from Cape Cod south and may enter freshwater. It reaches a length of 6 inches.

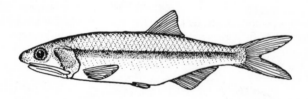

Figure 110

SALMON FAMILY, Salmonidae

The salmon family contains the salmon, trout, and whitefishes. These fishes are characterized by adipose fins and by an axillary process at the base of each pelvic fin. The family is divided into the salmon-trout subfamily, Salmoninae, and the whitefish subfamily, Coregoninae, which have often been considered as separate families.

The members of the salmon-trout subfamily, Salmoninae are fine scaled fishes, possessing well-developed teeth and coarse stubby gill rakers. This subfamily includes the Pacific salmon (*Oncorhynchus*), the trout (*Salmo*) which includes the Atlantic salmon, and the charrs (*Salvelinus*) which includes the brook trout, the Dolly Varden trout, and the lake trout.

These fishes were originally confined to the colder waters of the northern hemisphere, but through artificial propagation they have now been distributed to many parts of the world. All are either popular game fishes or important commercial food fishes. They are all cold water fishes, thriving best in water not warmer than 70° F. Both the Pacific salmon and the Atlantic salmon are anadromous, living in the sea, but spawning in freshwater. Many species of trout develop sea going races. Most trout live in both streams and lakes, except the lake trout which prefers lakes.

Trout are predaceous, feeding on a wide range of small animals, the larger individuals tending to become piscivorous. Most of the species of this family spawn in the fall, usually depositing their eggs on gravel beds. The eggs are covered and left to develop over winter, hatching in the early spring. Spring spawning races are known for several species.

The members of the whitefish subfamily, Coregoninae, are found only in the northern part of the Northern Hemisphere. They have large scales, weak jaws, and many have filamentous gill rakers. Most of them live in lakes, and with the exception of the western and arctic forms seldom enter streams.

They prefer cold water and are particularly abundant in the Great Lakes and other deep northern lakes. A number of species are restricted to the Great Lakes where they are well adapted to live in the deeper water far from shore, feeding on plankton and the deep bottom organisms.

Several species of the chubs go to depths of more than 750 feet in the Great Lakes. The cisco and the common whitefish seldom go this deep.

Most of the whitefishes spawn in the fall, and the eggs develop during the winter, hatching in the early spring. Although a few are caught by hook and line, most of them are caught in nets. Some species support an important commercial fisheries in the Great Lakes and in some of the larger lakes of Canada.

Many of the species exhibit much variation in different areas. This is particularly apparent in species confined in small lakes where they develop races with much deeper bodies than in the large Great Lakes.

1a. More than 100 scales in lateral line; maxillary extends behind center of eye (SALMON-TROUT)...........................2

1b. Less than 100 scales in lateral line; maxillary does not extend behind center of eye (WHITEFISHES)........................14

2a. Anal fin 13 to 19 rays; gill rakers of first arch 19 to 40; branchiostegals 13 to 19; vomer narrow and long with weak teeth; dorsal fin seldom with spots. (*Oncorhynchus*).......................4

2b. Anal fin with 9 to 12 rays; less than 20 gill rakers on first arch; branchiostegals usually 10 to 12; dorsal fin with spots...........3

3a. Body with dark spots on light background; less than 190 lateral line scales; teeth on shaft of vomer in alternating series or zigzag row. (*Salmo*) 8

3b. Body with light spots on dark background; more than 190 lateral line scales; no teeth on shaft of vomer. (*Salvelinus*)............12

4a. Lateral line scales numerous, more than 200...............PINK or HUMPBACK SALMON, *Onchorhynchus gorbuscha* (Walbaum)

Silvery fishes with bluish backs, caudal and adipose fin covered with black spots, those on caudal fin are coarse oblong spots. Weight up to 6 lbs. Anadromous, San Francisco to Alaska.

4b. Lateral line scales less than 160............................5
5a. Gill rakers short, 19-28 on first arch......................6
5b. Gill rakers long, 30 to 50 on first arch. Fig. 111.........SOCK-EYE or BLUEBACK SALMON, *Oncorhynchus nerka* (Walbaum)
Bluish above and silvery below; no spots. Length about 2 ft. and weight up to 8 lbs. Anadromous, California to Alaska. The LITTLE REDFISH or KOKANEE, *O. nerka kennerlyi* (Suckley) is a dwarfed landlocked form.

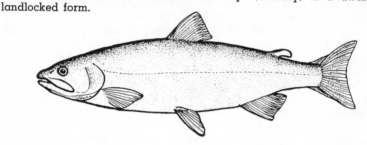

Figure 111

6a. Anal rays usually 13-15.......................................7
6b. Anal rays usually 15-17. Fig. 112....................CHINOOK or KING SALMON, *Oncorhynchus tschawytscha* (Walbaum)
Dusky or bluish above, silvery below. Flesh red. Back, dorsal and caudal fins usually profusely covered with spots. Weight up to 100 lbs. and length of 5 ft. Anadromous, San Francisco to Alaska.

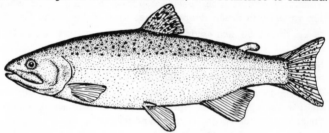

Figure 112

7a. Scales above lateral line usually 19-26; scales below lateral line usually 15-24 ....
......CHUM or DOG SALMON, *Oncorhynchus keta* (Walbaum)
Dusky above and light below. Fins more or less blackish. Flesh pale. Weight up to 12 pounds. Anadromous, San Francisco to Alaska.
7b. Scales above lateral line usually 25-31; scales below lateral line usually 23-34 ....
..COHO or SILVER SALMON, *Oncorhynchus kisutch* (Walbaum)

Bluish above, silvery below. Few spots on back, dorsal fin, and base of caudal fin. Small, length about 2 ft. and weight up to 8 pounds. Anadromous, Monterey to Alaska.

8a. Hyoid teeth (small teeth behind those on tip of tongue) always present; lateral line scales more than 150; red or pink streak on underside of each mandible; dorsal rays 9-11, usually 10. Fig. 113.
.................CUTTHROAT TROUT, *Salmo clarki* **Richardson**
Bluish on back, silvery on sides and belly. More or less profusely covered with small spots. Dorsal and caudal fins profusely spotted. Length ordinarily 10 to 15 inches. Weight up to six pounds, but some known to reach about 30 pounds. Many subspecies in Rocky Mountain and Pacific coast states; widely introduced in many areas. The GILA TROUT, *Salmo gilae* Miller from the Colorado River drainage in New Mexico is a closely related species.

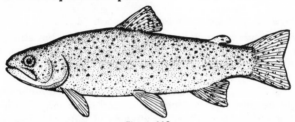

Figure 113

8b. Hyoid teeth absent; lateral line scales usually less than 150; no red or pink streak on underside of mandible; dorsal rays 10-13, usually 11-12 .....:..**9**
9a. Anal fin with 9 rays; adults with small "X" shape spots on sides. Fig. 114..............**ATLANTIC SALMON,** *Salmo salar* **Linnaeus**
Bluish brown backs, sides and belly silvery. Weight up to 10 pounds, but weights up to 100 pounds have been reported in Scotland. Anadromous, Atlantic Ocean, Delaware to Greenland and northern Europe.

The LANDLOCKED SALMON, *Salmo salar sebago* Girard is a smaller landlocked variety found in some eastern lakes.

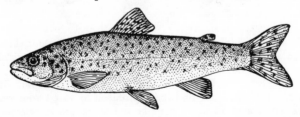

Figure 114

9b. Anal fin with 10-13 rays; sides usually with round spots except in some old brown trout......................................**10**

10a. Caudal fin without spots or with only a few restricted to dorsal portion. Fig. 115. . . . .
BROWN or LOCHLEVEN TROUT, *Salmo trutta fario* Linnaèus
Dark above, silvery below, back and sides more or less with numerous large spots. Length up to 2 feet. Widely introduced from Europe.

Figure 115

10b. Caudal fin profusely covered with spots. 11

11a. Dorsal, anal, and pelvic fins with some spots, but strongly emarginated with white offset by a dark bar; sides more or less brilliantly colored with yellow and orange; parr marks (vertical bars on sides of juveniles) retained by adults. Fig. 116. . . . .
. . . . .GOLDEN TROUT, *Salmo aguabonita* Jordan
Length usually 8 to 12 inches, although some may reach a length of 20 inches. Usually confined to streams of high altitudes, originally in the high Sierras of California, but introduced in several other areas. The GOLDEN TROUT of Volcano Creek or Golden Trout Creek (Kern River basin), California is closely related and sometimes regarded as a separate species, *Salmo roosevelti* Evermann.

Figure 116

11b. Dorsal and anal fins speckled, but not emarginated; side speckled and marked longitudinally with a more or less pinkish streak; no parr marks on adults. Fig. 117. . . . .
. . . . .RAINBOW TROUT, *Salmo gairdneri* Richardson
Bluish on back; sides and belly profusely covered with small spots. Reaches weights of 10 to 15 pounds, but some are known to be much larger. Originally in waters on west slope of the Rockies, but now widely introduced elsewhere. Many subspecies in western waters, including some anadromous forms.

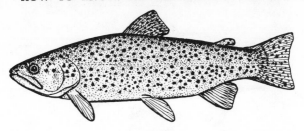

Figure 117

12a. Caudal fin deeply forked; body covered with light spots on dark background, belly sometimes spotted; fins not emarginated. Fig. 118.........**LAKE TROUT,** *Salvelinus namaycush* (Walbaum)
Color varies from light gray to almost black with profuse light spots. Reaches a length of over 3 feet and a weight of over 80 pounds. The Great Lakes and in colder lakes of the St. Lawrence, Hudson River, and the Great Lake drainages northwestward to headwaters of the Columbia and Fraser Rivers and into Alaska. Widely introduced in western lakes. A deep-bodied variety, *S. n. siscowet* (Agassiz) occurs in the deep waters of Lake Superior.

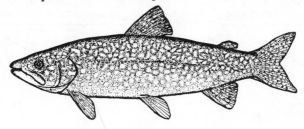

Figure 118

12b. Caudal fin not distinctly forked; body with light spots and some red spots on sides; fins strongly emarginated with whitish or cream color margins...**13**

13a. Back with mottled or "wormy" streaks on dark background; dorsal and caudal fins mottled. Fig. 119.............................
........**EASTERN BROOK TROUT,** *Salvelinus fontinalis* (Mitchill)
Back dark olive with somewhat lighter sides and belly (reddish in males). Sides with black and some red spots almost as large as pupil of eye. Dorsal and caudal fins rather mottled. Originally in certain waters from Minnesota eastward, but now distributed elsewhere. Several varieties, even anadromous forms are known. The BLUEBACK TROUT *Salvelinus oquassa* (Girard) of Rangeley Lakes, Maine and the SUNAPEE TROUT, *Salvelinus aureolus* Bean from Sunapee Lakes in New Hampshire are probably related forms.

51

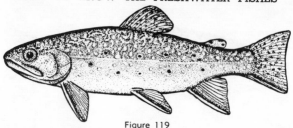

Figure 119

13b. Back with spots on dark background; dorsal and caudal fins not mottled. Fig. 120. . . . .
DOLLY VARDEN TROUT, *Salvelinus alpinus malma* (Walbaum)
Rather olivaceous to dark silvery with red spots about the size of eye on sides. Light spots on back. Length up to 20 inches (12 pounds). Streams on west slope of Rocky Mountains from northern California to Alaska and Siberia.

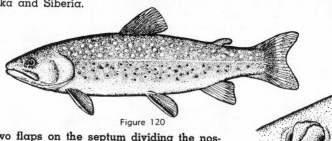

Figure 120

14a. Two flaps on the septum dividing the nostril (Fig. 121); gill rakers of first arch more than 23 15

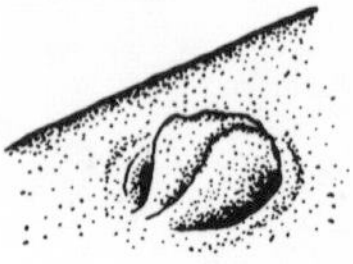

Figure 121

14b. Single flap on the septum dividing the nostril (Fig. 122); gill rakers of first arch less than 20 23

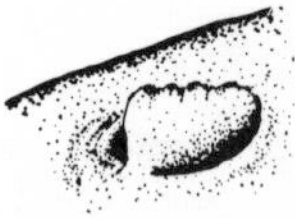

Figure 122

15a. Premaxillary wider than long, extending downward and backward forming a rounded or blunt snout (Fig. 123); gill rakers less than 32. Fig. 124. . . . .
. . .GREAT LAKES WHITEFISH, *Coregonus clupeaformis* (Mitchill)
Olivaceous above, white to silvery below. Length usually 12 to 20 inches, but may exceed 30 inches. Throughout the Great Lakes, various forms or subspecies in many large lakes extending from New England to Minnesota and northward.

Figure 123

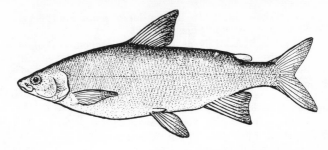

Figure 124

15b. Premaxillary longer than wide, extending downward and forward, forming a rather acute or pointed snout (Fig. 125); gill rakers more than 32..16

16a. Body deepest in front of center..17

16b. Body deepest at center........19

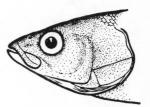

Figure 125

17a. Gill rakers less than 33...CHUB,
Coregonus johannae (Wagner)
Silvery fishes with dusky backs. Length 12 inches.
Deep water chub of Lakes Michigan and Huron.

17b. Gill rakers more than 33...................................18

18a. Small fishes, 6 to 8 inches long; mandible thin with knob or hook at tip. Fig. 126..............KIYI, Coregonus kiyi (Koeltz)

Silvery with dusky back. Several sub-species in deep waters of Lakes Superior, Michigan, and Ontario.

Figure 126

18b. **Larger fishes, 10 to 15 inches long; mandible thicker without knob or hook at tip. Figs. 127, 128** ....
............**BLACKFIN** or **BLUEFIN**, *Coregonus nigripinnis* (Gill)

Dark bluish above and silvery below with blue-black fins.

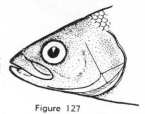

May reach a length of over 20 inches. Various subspecies in the deep waters of Lakes Superior, Michigan, Huron, Ontario, and some Canadian Lakes.

Figure 127

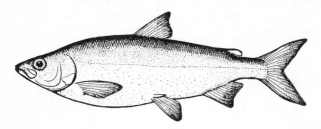

Figure 128

19a. **Gill rakers usually 43 to 52** ....
............**CISCO** or **LAKE HERRING**, *Coregonus artedi* LeSueur
Silvery below shading into a more or less dark bluish on back. Length usually 12 to 15 inches, but may exceed 24 inches. Many subspecies, known as lake herring or cisco (Fig. 129) in the Great Lakes and as tullibee (Fig. 130) in many large and deep lakes of the northern States and Canada. Those found in the Great Lakes tend to be more slender. A closely related species, *Coregonus hubbsi* (Koeltz), the **IVES LAKE**

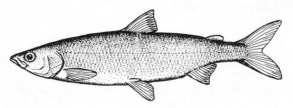

Figure 129

CISCO, is found in Ives Lake, Michigan.
PEAKNOSE CISCO, *Coregonus gemmifer* (Snyder). Similar to the cisco, but restricted to Bear Lake drainage, Idaho and Utah. Length 7 inches.

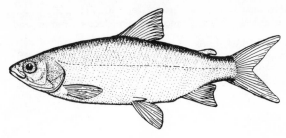

Figure 130

19b Gill rakers 34 to 43..20

20a Length 6 to 8 inches; mandible with knob or hook on tip. Fig. 131.
..............GREAT LAKES BLOATER, *Coregonus hoyi* (Gill)

Small, silvery with irridescent bluish back.
Deep waters of Lakes Superior, Michigan,
Huron, Ontario, and possibly some Canadian
Lakes.

Figure 131

20b. Length up to 12 to 15 inches; mandible thick and usually without knob at tip...21

21a. Lower jaw with considerable black pigment toward tip and projecting beyond upper jaw; body not very thin. Fig. 132........
..............SHORTNOSE CHUB, *Coregonus reighardi* (Koeltz)

Silvery white below and bluish above.
Length 15 inches. Various subspecies in
Lakes Superior, Michigan and Ontario.

Figure 132

21b. Lower jaw without much pigment and may or may not project
beyond upper jaw; body rather thin........................22

22a. Upper and lower jaw same length. Fig. 133................
  SHORTJAW CHUB, *Coregonus zenithicus* (Jordan and Evermann)

Silvery with dark back. Length about 15
inches. Found in deep waters of Lakes
Superior, Michigan, Huron, and in some
Canadian lakes.

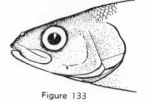

Figure 133

22b. Upper and lower jaws unequal, lower jaw projecting beyond
  upper jaw; lateral line scales over 77.......................
  ....LONGJAW CHUB, *Coregonus alpenae* (Koeltz)
Found in Lakes Michigan and Huron. A closely related species is
the cisco, *Coregonus bartletti* (Koeltz), with less than 77 scales, found
in Siskwit Lake on Isle Royale.

23a. Scales in lateral line less than 75, usually 55-60; size small,
  length usually less than 8 inches.........................PYG-
  MY WHITEFISH, *Coregonus coulteri* Eigenmann and Eigenmann
Dull silvery with a dusky back. The headwaters of the Columbia
River to Alaska. Recently reported from the deep waters of Lake
Superior by Dr. Paul H. Eschmeyer and Dr. Reeve M. Bailey in 1954.
  BEAR LAKE WHITEFISH, *Coregonus abyssicola* Snyder. Very simi-
lar, if not a subspecies, but differs in larger number of lateral line
scales, 69-78. Bear Lake drainage, Idaho and Utah.

23b. Scales in lateral line more than 75; fish larger; length usually
  more than 8 inches.......................................24

24a. Tip of snout below level of eye; profile of head rounded. Fig. 134.
  ROCKY MOUNTAIN WHITEFISH, *Coregonus williamsoni* Girard
Bluish above and silvery white below; all fins tipped with black.
Length up to about 15 inches. Various streams and lakes on west
slope of Rocky Mountains from Fraser River to Truckee River and
Lahonton Basin (Nevada) and on east side of Rocky Mountains in head-
waters of the Missouri and Saskatchewan Rivers.

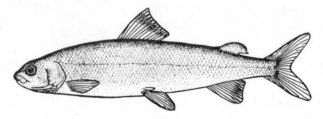

Figure 134

BONNEVILLE WHITEFISH, Coregonus *spilonotus* Snyder is very similar and may be a subspecies. It is restricted to Bear River Basin, Idaho and Utah.

CHISELMOUTH JACK, Coregonus *oregonius* (Jordan and Snyder). Very similar to Rocky Mountain whitefish except snout is very long and sharp and the adipose fin is very large. Lower tributaries of Columbia River, Oregon.

24b. Tip of snout not below level of eye; profile of head not rounded. Fig. 135.....ROUND WHITEFISH, Coregonus *cylindraceus* Pallas

Dark blue above and light silvery below. Length up to about 15 inches. Great Lakes except Lake Erie, and in some waters in New England and northwestward into Siberia.

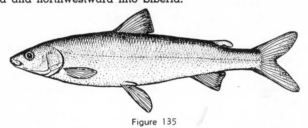

Figure 135

GRAYLING FAMILY, Thymallidae

The graylings are represented by several species found in Northern Europe, Asia and North America. They are similar to the trout, but readily recognized by the large sail-like dorsal fin. They spawn in the spring.

The graylings have a beautiful irridescent body colored purplish gray and silver with small spots, and have rows of bluish spots edged with rose or orange on the dorsal fin.

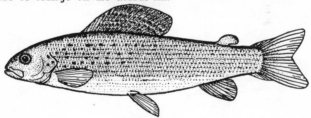

Figure 136

The AMERICAN GRAYLING, *Thymallus arcticus* (Pallas), (Fig. 136) is the only species found in North America, and is found in the cold streams of arctic America from Hudson Bay westward. In the United States isolated populations are found in several streams of the lower peninsula, in the Otter River of the upper Peninsula of Michigan, and in the headwaters of the Missouri River. They have been introduced elsewhere.

The grayling reaches a length of over fifteen inches and is considered one of the most popular game fishes.

SMELT FAMILY, Osmeridae

The American species of the smelt family, Osmeridae, are all found in the sea, but a number of species are anadromous and enter rivers in large spawning runs in the spring. The common Atlantic smelt, *Osmerus mordax* (Mitchill), has become landlocked in some eastern lakes, and was accidentally introduced thirty years ago into the Great Lakes where it now flourishes.

These are all small predaceous fishes seldom reaching a length of more than ten or twelve inches, but some species are highly prized for food.

In general they have slender, silvery bodies and are characterized by adipose fin, large scales and strong jaws with well developed teeth. They do not have the axillary process found at the base of the pelvic fin which is present in some of the related families possessing the adipose fin.

They are predaceous, feeding on all sorts of small aquatic animals, including small fishes.

1a. Teeth on vomer few and rather large (canine-like)............2

1b. Teeth on vomer numerous and small (not canine-like).........3

2a. Vomerine teeth moderate size, not fang-like; front of dorsal fin, definitely behind front of pelvic fins. Fig. 137..................
.................EULACHON, *Thaleichthys pacificus* (Richardson)
Dark above and silvery white below. Teeth shed during spawning season. Very oily and reputed to have been used as candles. Length up to 12 inches. Anadromous, entering streams on the Pacific coast from California northward.

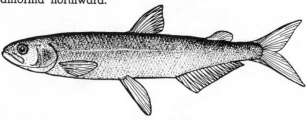

Figure 137

2b. Vomerine teeth consisting of 1 to 3 fang-like teeth on each side of the tip of the vomer; front of dorsal fin over or above front of pelvic fin. Fig. 138. .AMERICAN SMELT, *Osmerus mordax* (Mitchill)
Silvery below and dusky above. Length up to 12 inches. Anadromous, entering streams along the Atlantic coast from New York to Laborador. Landlocked in some waters of New York and New England

and in the Great Lakes. A similar species, *Osmerus sergeanti* Norris, is anadromous along the Atlantic coast from New York southward.

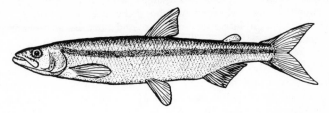

Figure 138

3a. Mouth large, 1.8 to 2.2 times in head length; maxillary extending to or beyond posterior margin of pupil; teeth large, but in one row on vomer and palatine.....................................
PUGET SOUND SMELT, *Spirinchus dilatus* Schultz and Chapman
Silvery with a rather dusky back. Length up to 12 inches. Marine, but enters freshwater from Oregon to British Columbia . The following related species are marine, but may be found in freshwater at the mouths of rivers.

NIGHT SURF SMELT, *Spirinchus starksi* (Fisk) occurs along the coast from Monterey, California to Washington.

SACRAMENTO SMELT, *Spirinchus thaleichthys* (Ayres) ranges into freshwater in California.

3b. Mouth small, 2.2 to 2.5 times in head length; maxillary extending not behind center of pupil of eye; teeth small and in 2 rows on vomer and palatine. Fig. 139..................................
...............FRESHWATER SMELT, *Hypomesus olidus* (Pallas)
Silvery with dark back. Length up to 12 inches. Anadromous, entering the streams on the Pacific coast from San Francisco to Alaska and Japan.

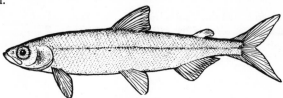

Figure 139

SURF SMELT, *Hypomesus pretiosus* (Girard). Differs in having a longer snout, more than 65 lateral line scales and the front of the dorsal fin before the front of the pelvic fins. Marine, found from Monterey, California northward, sometimes entering freshwater.

MUDMINNOW FAMILY, Umbridae

This family contains two genera with three American species. Mudminnows are soft-rayed and have the dorsal fin rather far back. They are more or less reddish brown and may be somewhat mottled. The lateral line is absent. Their upper jaw is non-protractile, lacking a groove separating it from the snout.

Mudminnows commonly inhabit swamps, muddy streams, and sloughs where they often bury themselves in the mud. They are hardy and have a remarkable resistance to drought and winter conditions. Mudminnows spawn in the early spring. They are reputed to be omnivorous, but feed heavily on small aquatic insects and crustaceans.

1a. Scale rows more than 50; anal fin rays 10-11. Fig. 140.........
............WESTERN MUDMINNOW, *Novumbra hubbsi* Schultz
Very similar to the central mudminnow in appearance, but differs in having a supermaxillary. Length 4 inches. Chehalis River, Washington.

Figure 140

1b. Scale rows less than 50; anal fin rays 7-8.....................2

2a. Body with longitudinal streaks. Fig. 141......................
.............EASTERN MUDMINNOW, *Umbra pygmaea* (DeKay)
Length 3 inches. Swamps and sluggish streams of Atlantic coastal plain, Long Island to Florida.

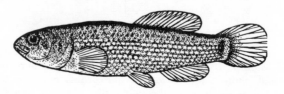

Figure 141

2b. Body without longitudinal streaks, but with more or less faint cross bars. Fig. 142....CENTRAL MUDMINNOW, *Umbra limi* (Kirtland)
Length usually about 2 inches, but sometimes exceeding 6 inches. Swamps and sluggish streams of upper Mississippi valley and Great Lakes region.

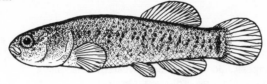

Figure 142

PIKE FAMILY, Esocidae

This family includes the muskellunge and the several species commonly known as various kinds of pike and pickerel, all belonging to the genus *Esox*. Very few groups of fishes have received as many common names as the several species comprising this family.

The members of this family are characterized by long cylindrical bodies with prominent jaws shaped like a duck's bill and armed with numerous fang-like teeth. They possess a soft dorsal fin which is located far back on the body.

Pickerel and pike vary in color from an olive brown to a pale silver with light undersides. They are marked with light or dark bars or spots depending on the species.

The several species of pike and pickerel are widely distributed through northern North America, Asia and Europe. They are highly predaceous, feeding on fishes and any other living animals small enough to seize. They spawn in the spring, scattering their eggs at random in shallow water where the eggs are fertilized and left to develop without any parental care. Pike grow very rapidly and some species reach a large size. The larger species are popular game fishes.

1a. Opercle with scales on upper half only (Fig. 143)..............2

1b. Opercle entirely scaled (Fig. 144)..............................3

Figure 143

Figure 144

2a. Pores on each side of ventral surface of lower jaw, six or more (Fig. 145); body with dark vertical bars or spots or with no marks on light background; lower half of cheek usually wholly or partially without scales. Fig. 146..... ....
.....................MUSKELLUNGE, *Esox masquinongy* Mitchill

Reaches a length of about 60 inches and weights up to 75 pounds are known. Three geographical races exist as follows; St. Lawrence and lower Great Lakes drainage; upper Ohio Valley; northwestern Wisconsin, northern Minnesota and adjacent Ontario.

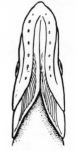

Figure 145

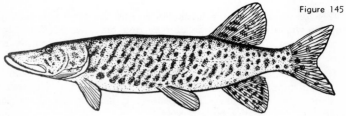

Figure 146

2b. Pores on each side of ventral surface of lower jaw, 5 or less (Fig. 147); body with small light spots on dark background (vertical bars in juveniles); cheek always entirely scaled (Fig. 148); variant known as silver pike has lost all body spots. Fig. 149.............................
.......NORTHERN PIKE, *Esox lucius* Linnaeus

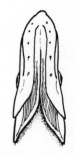

Figure 147

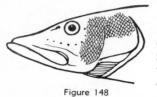

Figure 148

Reaches a length of over 40 inches and a weight of over 30 pounds. Eastern U. S. north of the Ohio River and northwestward into Alaska and in northern Siberia and Europe.

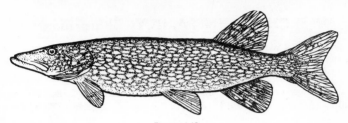

Figure 149

3a. Sides and back marked with dark network; scales of lateral line 125; branchiostegal rays 14-16. Fig. 150........................
........................CHAIN PICKEREL, *Esox niger* LeSueur
This is the common pickerel of the New England States. It reaches a length of over 24 inches and a weight of 10 pounds. East of the Appalachians from the St. Lawrence southward and along the Gulf coast to Texas.

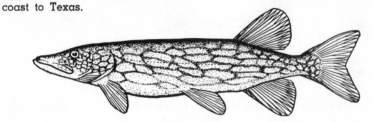

Figure 150

3b. Sides and back marked with dark wavy or wormy vertical streaks; lateral line scales 105; branchiostegal rays 11-13. Fig. 151.................REDFIN PICKEREL, *Esox americanus* Gmelin
Very small, seldom reaching a length of more than 12 inches. Atlantic coastal plain and Gulf States.

The GRASS or MUD PICKEREL, *Esox vermiculatus* LeSueur, is similar in appearance and size to the redfin pickerel, but the head is longer. It is usually considered as a subspecies of the redfin pickerel. Iowa eastward through Ohio valley and south to Texas.

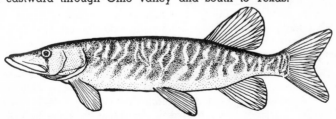

Figure 151

CHARACIN FAMILY, Characidae

The Characins form a large family of about 300 species found mostly in South America and Africa. They possess an adipose fin. They have a wide range of form and habits.

Some species extend up into Mexico, and, at least, one species ranges to the Rio Grande River. This is the MEXICAN TETRA, *Astyanax fasciatus mexicanus* (Filippi) (Fig. 152) which is found in southern Texas, and also in the lower Colorado River drainage of Arizona and New Mexico. It reaches a length of about 4 inches.

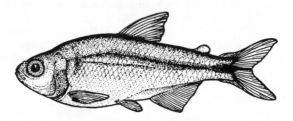

Figure 152

SUCKER FAMILY, Catostomidae

This family is closely allied to the following minnow family. The suckers are softrayed fishes and possess a toothless and more or less sucker-like protractile mouth with thick lips. The last pharyngeal arch bears a row of numerous comb-like teeth (see Fig. 32) which distinguishes the suckers from the minnows which have either more than one row of teeth, or one row with only a few (5) teeth. Suckers usually have more than 10 dorsal rays, whereas, most native minnows have no more than 10 dorsal rays.

The heads are naked, and the body is covered with smooth cycloid scales. They are extremely bony as the ribs, including a set of accessory ribs, are distributed from the head to the tip of the tail. Otherwise, the flesh of most members of this family is quite edible.

This family contains many species which are quite widely distributed in the United States and furnish an important group of our so-called forage fishes. They are mostly omnivorous, feeding on the bottom where they eat a large variety of animal matter as well as some plant material.

They spawn in the spring, many species making spectacular spawning "runs" up small tributary streams. They are very prolific, and the eggs are scattered at random and develop without any parental care. During spawning season the males in some species may develop tubercles on the head, brighter colors and elongated anal fins.

1a. Dorsal fin long with 25 to 40 rays............................2

1b. Dorsal fin short with 10 to 18 rays........................4

2a. Lateral line scales more than 50; eyes in back part of head; head small and abruptly more slender than body; body is 6-7 times length of head.......................................*Cycleptus*
BLUE SUCKER, *Cycleptus elongatus* (LeSueur). Fig. 153. Dark back and dusky silvery on sides. Reaches a length of over 2 feet. In large rivers from southern Minnesota and Wisconsin to Tennessee and Mexico.

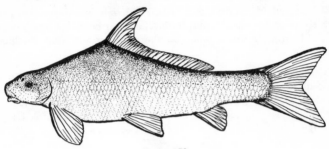

Figure 153

2b. Lateral line scales less than 45; eyes in front part of head; head large and not abruptly more slender than body................3

3a. Distance from eye to lower posterior angle of preopercle about 3/4 distance to upper corner of gill cleft; subopercle widest at middle; pharyngeal arch thick, triangular in cross section.............
....BUFFALOFISHES, *Ictiobus*
This genus contains three species. They are large golden or reddish brown fishes with deep bodies.
LARGEMOUTH BUFFALOFISH, *Ictiobus cyprinellus* (Valenciennes). Fig. 154. Mouth large with upper lip about level with lower margin of eye. Reaches a length of about 3 feet. North Dakota and Lake Erie to Alabama and Texas.

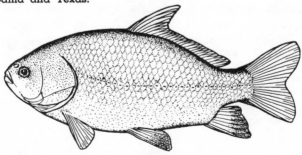

Figure 154

65

SMALLMOUTH BUFFALOFISH, *Ictiobus bubalus* (Rafinesque). Mouth small (Fig. 155) with upper lip far below lower margin of eye; back quite elevated. Reaches a length of 2½ feet. Southern Minnesota to Michigan and south to Mexico.

Figure 155

BLACK OR MONGREL BUFFALOFISH, *Ictiobus niger* (Rafinesque). Mouth same as for smallmouth buffalofish, but back not much elevated. Reaches length of three feet. Southern Minnesota and Michigan to Texas.

3b. Distance from eye to lower posterior angle of preopercle about equal to distance to upper corner of gill cleft; subopercle widest below middle; pharyngeal arch almost paper thin..............
..................................**CARPSUCKERS,** *Carpiodes*

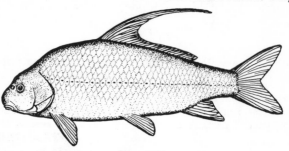

Figure 156

Color more or less silvery. Some may reach a length of over 20 inches. This genus contains four species in the United States.

QUILLBACK CARPSUCK-ER, *Carpiodes cyprinus* (Le-Sueur). Fig. 156. No nipple-like structure on lower lip (Fig. 157); anterior dorsal rays elongated, longer than base of fin; lateral line scales 37-40; nostril posterior to middle of mouth (Fig. 158).

Figure 157

Figure 158

Southern Manitoba and Great Lakes region to Kansas and western Florida.

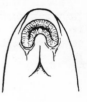

HIGH FIN CARPSUCKER, *Carpiodes velifer* (Rafinesque). Nipple-like structure on lower lip (Fig. 159); anterior dorsal rays much elongated; mouth mostly posterior to nostrils (Fig. 160); front of upper lip under nostrils; lateral line scales 33-37. Minnesota to Pennsylvania and south to Tennessee.

Figure 159

Figure 160

CARPSUCKER, *Carpiodes carpio* (Rafinesque). Fig. 161. Nipple-like structure on lower lip (Fig. 159); anterior dorsal rays only slightly elongated, not reaching more than ½ the base of the fin; mouth mostly posterior to nostrils; front of upper lip almost under nostril (Fig. 162); lateral line scales 33-37. Montana to Pennsylvania and south to Tennessee and Texas.

Figure 162

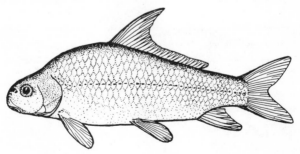

Figure 161

RIVER CARPSUCKER, *Carpiodes forbesi* Hubbs. No nipple-like structure on lower lip (Fig. 157); anterior dorsal rays only slightly elongated, not reaching much more than ½ the length of the fin base; mouth mostly anterior to nostrils (Fig. 163); nostril above or behind middle of mouth; back not much elevated. Southern Minnesota to Kansas.

Figure 163

4a. Lateral line absent or incomplete in adults.....................5
4b. Lateral line complete in adults...............................6
5a. Lateral line partly or almost complete; each scale with a distinct spot, forming a pattern of rows of dotted lines on sides; mouth inferior and horizontal..............................*Minytrema*
SPOTTED SUCKER, *Minytrema melanops* (Rafinesque). Fig. 164. Silvery, distinctly characterized by a spot on each scale. Reaches a length of about 18 inches. Larger streams, southern Minnesota to Pennsylvania and south to Texas and Florida.

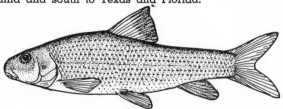

Figure 164

5b. Lateral line absent; sides of young with longitudinal stripe which breaks up into blotches in adults; mouth subterminal and oblique ....CHUBSUCKERS, *Erimyzon*
Small silvery fishes reaching a length of about 10 inches.
LAKE CHUBSUCKER, *Erimyzon succetta* (Lacépède). Fig. 165. Longitudinal scale rows 36-38. Eastern Minnesota to New England and south to Florida and Texas.

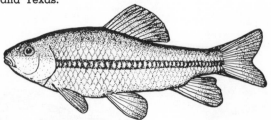

Figure 165

CREEK CHUBSUCKER, *Erimyzon oblongus* (Mitchill). Longitudinal scale rows 39-41. Wisconsin to New England and south to Alabama and Texas.

ALABAMA CHUBSUCKER, *Erimyzon tenuis* (Agassiz). Fig. 166. Differs in that first dorsal ray is as long as base of dorsal fin. Gulf drainage of Mississippi, Alabama, and western Florida.

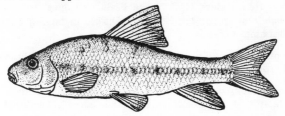

Figure 166

6a. Pronounced hump on back just behind head..........*Xyrauchen*
HUMPBACK SUCKER, *Xyrauchen texanus* (Abbott). Fig. 167. Rather olivaceous. Reaches length of 2 feet. Lower Colorado River.

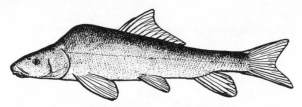

Figure 167

6b. No pronounced hump on back just behind head...............7
7a. Scales less than 55 in lateral line and not crowded anteriorly...8
7b. Scales more than 55 in lateral line and crowded anteriorly......11
8a. Top of head between eyes concave; swim bladder in 2 parts....
....................................**HOGSUCKERS,** *Hypentelium*
Dusky silver, mottled with black. Reaches a length of about 10-12 inches.

HOGSUCKER, *Hypentelium nigricans* (LeSueur). Fig. 168. Dorsal rays 11; lateral line scales 46; total pectoral rays for both sides 34; dark saddle crosses back before dorsal fin. Minnesota to New York and south to Oklahoma and Alabama.

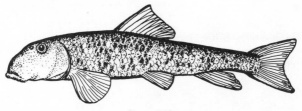

Figure 168

Hypentelium roanokense Raney and Lachner. Dorsal rays 11, but differs from hogsucker in having 41 lateral line scales and in having total pectoral rays for both sides 31; dark saddle not developed before dorsal fin. Headwaters of Roanoke River, Virginia.

Hypentelium etowanum (Jordan). Differs in having only 10 dorsal rays. Alabama River.

8b. Top of head usually convex between eyes; swim bladder obsolete or in three parts..9

9a. Swim bladder obsolete; head small; pectoral fins large, 1½ times the length of the head; cartilaginous sheath inside of each jaw (Fig. 169) ....*Thoburnia*
Small dusky silvery fishes, reaching a length of 8 to 10 inches.

Thoburnia rhothoeca (Thoburn). Fig. 170. Restricted to the headwaters of the James and Kanawha Rivers and possibly, Potomac River, Virginia.

Thoburnia hamiltoni Raney and Lachner. Upper Roanoke River system, Virginia.

Figure 169

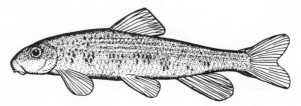

Figure 170

9b. Swim bladder in 3 parts; head large; no cartilaginous sheath inside of jaws...10

10a. Premaxillary not protractile; lower lip completely divided into two separate lobes (Fig. 171)........................*Lagochila*

RABBITMOUTH SUCKER, *Lagochila lacera* Jordan and Brayton. Length up to 18 inches. Larger streams of the central Mississippi valley.

Figure 171

10b. Premaxillaries protractile; lower lips with both sides joined and not divided (Fig. 172)..................REDHORSE, *Moxostoma*

More or less silvery to reddish brown, usually dark on back; fins usually tend to be reddish. Some reach a length of over 24 inches; but many are much smaller.

Figure 172

SILVER REDHORSE, *Moxostoma anisurum* (Rafinesque). Halves of lower lip meet at an angle (Fig. 172); creases of lips are broken into papillae. Manitoba to St. Lawrence drainage and south to northern Alabama and Missouri.

Moxostoma collapsum (Cope). Similar to the silver redhorse except mouth is smaller. Roanoke River, Virginia southward in coastal streams.

NORTHERN REDHORSE, *Moxostoma aureolum* (Le-Sueur). Fig. 173. Halves of lower lip meet in a more or less straight line (Fig. 174), creases of lips are slightly broken into papillae at ends; head goes 4.3 to 5.4 times into standard length. Central and eastern Canada south to Hudson River and to Kansas, not found in much of the Ohio drainage.

Figure 174

Moxostoma coregonus (Cope). Similar to the northern redhorse. Catawba and Yadkin River systems, North Carolina.

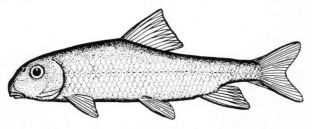

Figure 173

SHORTHEAD REDHORSE, *Moxostoma breviceps* (Cope). Fig. 175. Similar to northern redhorse, but differs in having 10 pelvic rays, a strongly falcate dorsal fin, and the upper caudal lobe narrower and longer than the lower lobe. Ohio River drainage in Ohio, Pennsylvania, and Kentucky.

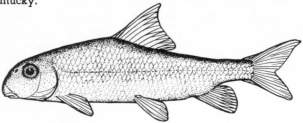

Figure 175

TEXAS REDHORSE, *Moxostoma congestum* (Baird and Girard). Similar to northern redhorse, but usually has 12 dorsal rays instead of 13; dorsal fin is very low and small. Rio Grande River and vicinity, Texas.

CAROLINA REDHORSE, *Moxostoma conus* (Cope). Very similar to shorthead redhorse, but has 9 pelvic rays instead of 10. The dorsal fin is strongly falcate. North Carolina.

JUMPING REDHORSE, *Moxostoma cervinum* (Cope). Fig. 176. Dark saddles on back and light longitudinal streaks on sides; dorsal fin with black tip. Coastal streams from James River to Neuse River systems, Virginia.

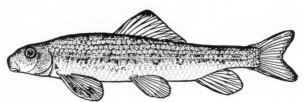

Figure 176

STRIPPED JUMPROCK, *Moxostoma rupiscartes* Jordan and Jenkins. Very similar to the jumping redhorse except tips of fins are dusky instead of black. North Carolina southward in Santee, Savannah, Altamaha, and Chattahoochee River systems.

GREATER JUMPROCK, *Moxostoma lachneri* Robins and Raney. Related to stripped jumprock. Caudal fin dusky except for milky white lower ray. Appalachicola River system, Georgia.

RIVER REDHORSE, *Moxostoma carinatum* Cope. Lips are very large and thick; dorsal fin somewhat falcate; upper lobe of caudal fin is much longer than lower lobe. Differs from other redhorses in very heavy pharyngeal arch and pharyngeal teeth. Iowa to St. Lawrence River and south to northern Georgia and Alabama.

THICKLIP REDHORSE, *Moxostoma crassilabre* (Cope). Head very short and blunt, very similar to the eastern redhorse. Streams of eastern North Carolina.

WHITE MULLET, *Moxostoma pappillosum* (Cope). More or less silvery; lower lip with a very deep cleft. Coastal streams from Roanoke River, Virginia to Georgia.

ROBUST REDHORSE, *Moxostoma robustum* (Cope). Similar to stripped jumprock but head is shorter and deeper. Yadkin to Altamaha River systems in North Carolina southward to Georgia.

BIGEYE REDHORSE, *Moxostoma ariommum* Robins and Raney. Lower lip very papillose; very concave between the eyes. Roanoke River, Virginia.

BLACK REDHORSE, *Moxostoma duquesni* (LeSueur). Rather slender with finer scales, 44-47 scales in lateral line instead of 39-45 as in other redhorses; 10 pelvic rays instead of 9 as in other redhorses except the shorthead redhorse. Lips broken into course papillae, no spots on scale bases. Southern Minnesota to Ontario and south to Alabama and Oklahoma in Mississippi and Great Lakes drainages.

GOLDEN REDHORSE, *Moxostoma erythrurum* (Rafinesque). Lips with no papillae, lower halves meet at a sharp angle (Fig. 177). Similar to the greater redhorse except that scale bases have no black spots and the dorsal fin is rather falcate and is black at the tip and near the margin. Minnesota and southern Ontario south to Georgia and Oklahoma. *M. lachrymale* (Cope) in North Carolina is very similar if not the same.

Figure 177

GREATER REDHORSE, *Moxostoma valenciennsei* Jordan. Lips with creases not broken into papillae, lower halves meet at an angle. Similar to the golden redhorse except the dorsal fin is not falcate, and the tip is whitish and the scale bases have dark spots. Minnesota and Great Lakes, St. Lawrence area south to Iowa and Illinois. Absent in most of the Ohio drainage.

EASTERN REDHORSE, *Moxostoma macrolepidotum* (LeSueur). Similar to the northern redhorse except that the head is longer, 4.2 to 4.35 times in standard length. Restricted to streams of Delaware and Chesapeake Bay where it is the only redhorse present.

BLACKTAIL REDHORSE, *Moxostoma poecilurum* Jordan. Fig. 178. Similar to the northern redhorse except the lower lobe of the caudal fin is black and is narrower and longer than the upper lobe. Coastal streams of the Gulf of Mexico.

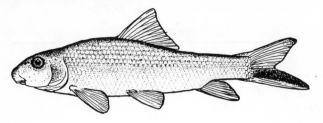

Figure 178

11a. **Mouth usually with notches in corners. Fig. 179**...............
............................**MOUNTAIN SUCKER,** *Pantosteus*

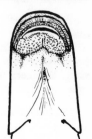

The characters for this group are not easily defined. The species are best identified by distribution. They are dusky above and pale below; breeding males have orange to red lateral band. Most of them reach a .length of 10-12 inches.

Figure 179

CHISELMOUTH SUCKER, *Pantosteus delphinus* (Cope). Fig. 180. Peduncle slender; lateral line scales more than 90. Upper Colorado river drainage.

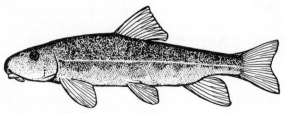

Figure 180

74

MOUNTAIN SUCKER, *Pantosteus jordani* Evermann. Stout peduncle; lateral line scales 90-100 and crowded anteriorly. Upper Columbia river drainage and headwaters of the Missouri.

FLATNOSE MOUNTAIN SUCKER, *Pantosteus platyrhynchus* (Cope). Bonneville Basin and Snake River drainage Utah and Wyoming.

COARSESCALE MOUNTAIN SUCKER, *Pantosteus plebius* (Baird and Girard). Head large; lateral line scales about 80. Rio Grande River, Colorado to Mexico.

Pantosteus clarki (Baird and Girard). Lateral line scales about 70. Lower Colorado River.

SANTA ANA MOUNTAIN SUCKER, *Pantosteus santanae* Snyder. Southern California.

LAHONTAN MOUNTAIN SUCKER, *Pantosteus lahontan* Rutter. Fig. 181. Lahontan Basin, Nevada.

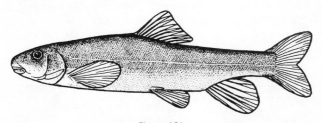

Figure 181

11b. Mouth without any notches in the corners.....................12

12a. Mouth large and terminal; upper lip thin and both lips rather smooth and without any papillae....................*Chasmistes*
SHORTNOSE KLAMATH LAKE SUCKER, *Chasmistes brevirostris* Cope. Fig. 182. Dusky above, pale below. Length 16 inches. Klamath Lake, Oregon.

JUNE SUCKER, *Chasmistes liorus* Jordan. Scales of back and sides with dark punctulations. Length 18 inches. Utah Lake, Utah.

COUIA, *Chasmistes cujus* Cope. Pale olive. Restricted to Pyramid Lake, Nevada.

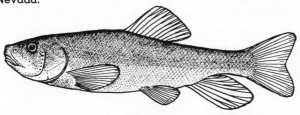

Figure 182

12b. Mouth small and subterminal; upper lip thick and both lips rough and covered with papillae...............................13

13a. Snout without pronounced hump....................*Catostomus*
Color mostly silvery shading to dark on backs. Some species develop reddish streaks on sides during spawning season. This genus may be divided into two groups represented by the fine scaled suckers with more than 80 lateral line scales and by the coarse scaled suckers with less than 80 scales in the lateral line. East of the Rockies, each group is represented by one species. West of the Rockies many species of both groups have developed in the isolated stream systems. Many reach a length of 18 inches.

WHITE SUCKER, *Catostomus commersoni* (Lacépède). Fig. 183. Lateral line scales 55-70. Very common east of the Rockies from southern Canada south to Colorado, Missouri and Georgia. It is represented on the Great Plains from Montana to Mexico by *C. commersoni suckli* Girard. Introduced into Colorado River system.

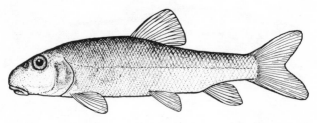

Figure 183

UTAH SUCKER, *Catostomus ardens* Jordan and Gilbert. Lateral line scales 70-72. Bonneville Basin, Utah.

ROSYSIDE SUCKER, *Catostomus fecundus* (Cope and Yarrow). Lateral line scales 64-75. Bonneville Basin and upper Snake River, Utah and Wyoming.

COARSESCALE SUCKER, *Catostomus macrocheilus* Girard. Lateral line scales 65-75. Columbia River.

GILA SUCKER, *Catostomus insignis* Baird and Girard. About 56 lateral line scales. Gila River system, Arizona.

WARNER LAKE COARSESCALE SUCKER, *Catostomus warnerensis* Snyder. Lateral line scales 73-79. Warner Lake Basin.

KLAMATH LARGESCALE SUCKER, *Catostomus snyderi* Gilbert. Lateral line scales 69-77. Above falls of Klamath River, Oregon.

CALIFORNIA SUCKER, *Catostomus occidentalis* Ayres. Fig. 184. Lateral line scales about 75. 12-14 dorsal rays. Widespread with many subspecies in central California.

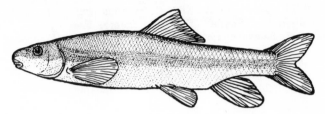

Figure 184

EASTERN LONGNOSE SUCKER, *Catostomus catostomus* (Forster). Fig. 185. Snout is long and pointed; lateral line scales 90-117. Widely distributed east of the Rockies from Alaska to Maine and represented in the upper Missouri and in the Columbia Rivers by *C. catostomus griseus* Girard.

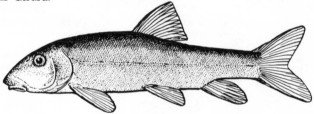

Figure 185

FLANNELMOUTH SUCKER, *Catostomus latipinnis* Baird and Girard. Fig. 186. Lateral line scales more than 80; lower lip very thick and wide (Fig. 187); 10-11 dorsal rays. Colorado River drainage.

C. latipinnis discobolus Cope is in the upper and middle Colorado River drainage, and has from 98 to 105 lateral line scales.

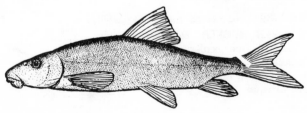

Figure 186

SACRAMENTO SMALLSCALE SUCKER, *Catostomus microps* Rutter. Lateral line scales 81-87. Sacramento River, California.

LOWER KLAMATH SUCKER, *Catostomus rimiculus* Gilbert and Snyder. Fig. 188. Lateral line scales 81-93. Below falls of Klamath River, Oregon.

COLUMBIA FINESCALE SUCKER, *Catostomus columbianus* (Eigenmann and Eigenmann). Lateral line scales 100-111. Middle and Lower Columbia River.

Figure 187

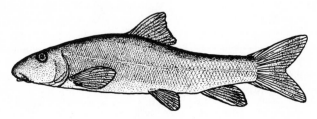

Figure 188

TAHOE SUCKER, *Catostomus tahoensis* Gill and Jordan. Fig. 189. Lateral line scales 83-92. Lake Tahoe, California and Nevada.

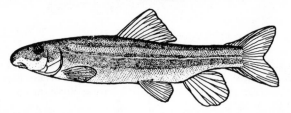

Figure 189

13b. Snout with pronounced hump (Fig. 190)................*Deltistes*

LOST RIVER SUCKER, *Deltistes luxatus* (Cope). Lateral line scales more than 80; snout is humped. Pale below, dark above. Reaches a length of three feet. Klamath River drainage, Oregon.

Figure 190

78

MINNOW FAMILY, Cyprinidae

The minnow family is the largest group of our freshwater fishes, containing more species and more individuals than any other family. Only fishes belonging to this family are true minnows, although the name is often incorrectly applied to some small fishes in other families. Most minnows are small, but that is not true for all as several species reach a length of three to five feet.

Minnows are closely related to the sucker family, but differ in several respects. In general, they lack the sucker-like mouth, although several species have mouths closely resembling those of suckers. They lack teeth in the mouth, but have well-developed pharyngeal teeth as in the suckers. However, the pharyngeal teeth of the minnows are not as numerous as those of the suckers and follow a plan of more than one row (Fig. 35), usually 2 rows in our native minnows (3 rows in introduced carp and goldfish). In some minnows the outer rows may fail to develop, leaving only one row on each arch, but these never bear more than 5 teeth (6 in one species) on a side. The teeth have been used as an important diagnostic character and the dental formula is usually written from left to right. A formula of 2, 4-4, 2 may be interpreted as 2 teeth in the left outer row, 4 teeth in the left inner row, 4 teeth in the right inner row, and 2 teeth in the right outer row. To observe these teeth, they must be carefully dissected.

Most minnows lack spines except in the several introduced forms, carp and goldfish, and in several peculiar species in the deserts of the southwest. Most minnows have less than 10 dorsal rays, although several including the carp and goldfishes exceed this number.

Minnows are very important fishes. Their great abundance and usual small size make them valuable as food for other fishes. Various minnows utilize the minute animal and plant life of our waters, and in turn furnish food for the game fishes. Many species have long been utilized as bait, and at present the bait industry has become a major industry in many parts of the United States. A few of the larger minnows are used for food. The carp have supported a large fishery industry ever since their introduction. Minnows have a complete series of multiple ribs from head to tip of tail which makes them excessively bony. This factor together with the coarse flesh and muddy flavor of many species does not make them very popular for food.

Minnows feed on almost every type of food found in our waters. Some are mud feeders, others are vegetarian, and many prey upon the various forms of minute animal life. Many species are omnivorous. Most species spawn in the spring or early summer, but spawning habits of the various species differ very much. Many are random spawners and give no care to their eggs. Some, such as the carp and the western squawfish. crowd into shallow waters and deposit their eggs with great splashing. Other species deposit their eggs on special types of bottom and cover the eggs. A few species select special places, such as the underside of logs and stones, for their eggs and the males guard them until they hatch.

Some minnows are rather difficult to key to species. Most keys use the type and number of pharyngeal teeth as one of the main diagnostic characters. Teeth are difficult for anyone but an expert ichthyologist, and as teeth often show anomalies, they are sometimes difficult for an ichthyologist. The following keys have been devised in an attempt to avoid the use of teeth as much as possible and result in quite an artificial separation of the various genera and species. Often it is difficult to give precise characters for separating some species and even genera. Individual variations in characters, such as number of fin rays, may overlap and without a large series of individuals for averaging, the key may not always function.

1a. More than 12 dorsal rays.....................................2

1b. Less than 12 dorsal rays......................................3

2a. With 2 barbels on each side of upper jaw; anterior spine in dorsal and anal fin..*Cyprinus*
EUROPEAN CARP, *Cyprinus carpio* Linneaus. Fig. 191. Reddish brown on back to silver below. Length up to 30 inches. Widely introduced in the U. S. from Europe, originating in Asia.

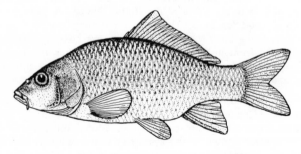

Figure 191

2b. **Without barbels on upper jaw; anterior spine in dorsal and anal fin** .... *Carassius*

GOLDFISH, *Carassius auratus* (Linneaus). Fig. 192. Color varies from reddish gold to brown. Length up to 12 inches. Introduced and liberated in many parts of U. S.

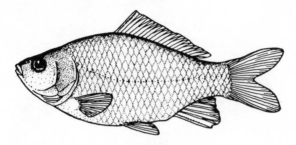

Figure 192

3a. **Dorsal fin without spines** 4

3b. **Dorsal fin with double spines** 37

cartilaginous ridge

4a. **Lower jaw with distinct inner cartilaginous or horny ridge. Fig. 193** 5

4b. **Lower jaw without a distinct inner cartilaginous ridge** 7

Figure 193

5a. **Cartilaginous ridge confined to lower jaw; intestine wrapped many times about swim bladder** ....*Campostoma*

STONEROLLER, *Campostoma anomalum* (Rafinesque). Figs. 194, 195. Brownish, more or less mottled; peritoneum black and shows through skin on belly; dorsal and anal fins wtih dark cross bar; about 53 scales in lateral line. Length 8 inches. Spring males with reddish color and numerous tubercules. Various subspecies found from Minnesota to Texas and eastward.

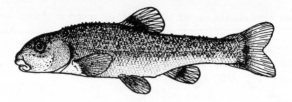

Figure 194

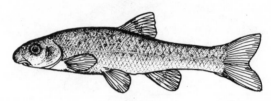

Figure 195

Campostoma ornatum Girard. Similar to stoneroller except scales are smaller; 72 scales in lateral line; head and mouth are larger. Rio Grande drainage, Texas.

5b. Cartilaginous or horny ridge in both upper and lower jaws; intestine not wrapped about swim bladder, but of several free loops or coils and about twice the length of body................6

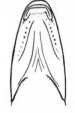

6a. Dorsal rays about 10; ridges inside of jaws covered by heavy and not easily removed horny sheaths. (Fig. 196)...................*Acrocheilus*

Figure 196

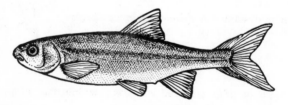

Figure 197

CHISELMOUTH, *Acrocheilus alutaceum* Agassiz and Pickering. Fig. 197. Dark, belly somewhat lighter; caudal fin very long. Teeth 4-5. Length 12 inches. Columbia River drainage of Washington, Oregon, and Nevada.

6b. Dorsal rays usually 8 (7-8); ridges inside of jaws covered by easily removed horny sheaths...............................*Eremichthys*
DESERT MINNOW, *Eremichthys acros* Hubbs and Miller. Fig. 198. Warm Springs, Soldier Creek, Nevada.

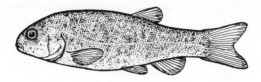

Figure 198

7a. Lateral line scales more than 100; a barbel present at end of maxillary ....*Tinca*
TENCH, *Tinca tinca* (Linneaus). Fig. 199. A fine scaled minnow introduced from Europe into parts of the western U. S.

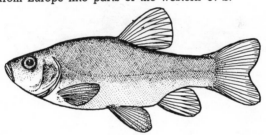

Figure 199

7b. Lateral line scales less than 100; if more than 100, the barbel is absent..8

8a. Premaxillaries (protractile) separated from snout by a complete groove (caution: an apparently complete groove may not be complete but may be connected by a hidden bridge of skin) (Fig. 200) 14

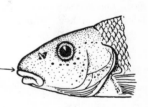

Figure 200

8b. Premaxillaries (not protractile) not separated completely from head, but connected by a bridge of skin or frenum to tip of snout; this bridge may be a slight connection hidden in the groove in several western species. (Fig. 201) 9

Figure 201

9a. Lower lip not modified by side lobes but continuous with central part 10

9b. Lower lip modified by fleshy side lobes separate from the central part. (See Fig. 208)..12

10a. Barbel usually at end of maxillary. (See Fig. 215)...*Rhinichthys* Most of the various forms described for this genus can be reduced to subspecies of three species. The snout distinctly overhangs upper lip.

BLACKNOSE DACE, *Rhinichthys atratulus* (Hermann). Fig. 202. More or less blackish above, silvery below, with lateral band (males rosy on sides); snout rather short. Teeth 2, 4-4, 2. Length 4 inches. Several subspecies in streams from North Dakota to the St. Lawrence drainage and south to Nebraska and North Carolina.

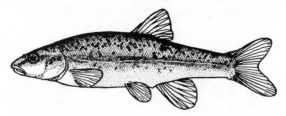

Figure 202

LONGNOSE DACE, *Rhinichthys cataractae* (Valenciennes). Fig. 203. More or less black above, silvery below; back and sides may be mottled; snout very elongated. Spring males reddish. Teeth 2, 4-4, 2. Length 5 inches. Many subspecies over most of U. S. except southeastern coastal region.

Figure 203

WESTERN SPECKLED DACE, *Rhinichthys osculus* (Girard). Fig. 204. Similar to blacknose dace; premaxillary may be connected to snout by a slight hidden frenum. Many subspecies west of the Rockies in coastwise streams of Washington and Oregon, and in Columbia drainage south to southern California, Lahonton basin and Colorado River drainage.

Figure 204

10b. No barbel at end of maxillary............................11
11a. Lateral line scales about 75; maxillary extends to front of eye..
....*Mylopharodon*

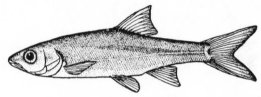

Figure 205

HARDHEAD, *Mylopharodon conocephalus* (Baird and Girard). Fig. 205. Dark above, pale below. Teeth 2, 4-5, 2. Large size, length to 3 feet. Sacramento River system, California.

DESERT MINNOW, *Moapa coriacea* Hubbs and Miller. Specimens with a slight frenum or bridge of skin connecting premaxillary to snout will key here. (See Fig. 228, couplet 26a.)

Tiaroga cobitis Girard. If lips are considered to be without side lobes, specimens will key here. (See Fig. 207, couplet 12a.)

11b. Lateral line scales about 100; maxillary does not reach front of
    eye ....*Orthodon*

SACRAMENTO BLACKFISH, *Orthodon microlepidotus* (Ayres). Fig. 206. Plain olivaceous above, light below. Teeth 6-6(5). Length 12-16 inches. Sacramento River system, California.

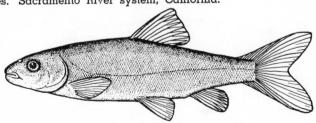

Figure 206

12a. Scales well developed mostly along lateral line; central part of lower lip fleshy ....*Tiaroga*

Tiaroga cobitis Girard. Fig. 207. Slender body; olivaceous with small caudal spot; pair of yellowish spots at base of caudal fin. Lower lips are very thick and lateral creases give appearance of side lobes. Teeth 1, 4-4, 1. Length 2½ inches. Gila River, Arizona.

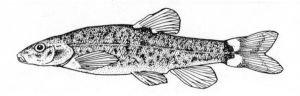

Figure 207

12b. Scales well developed on most of body; central part of lower lip not fleshy..13

13a. Central part of lower tip protrudes like a tongue (Fig. 208); no barbel present ....*Exoglossum*

CUTLIPS MINNOW, *Exoglossum maxillingua* (LeSueur). Fig. 209. Dusky olivaceous above, lighter below. Teeth 1, 4-4, 1. Length 6 inches. St. Lawrence and Lake Ontario south into Virginia.

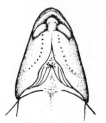

Figure 208

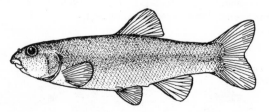

Figure 209

13b. Central part of lip thin, but not protruding. (Fig. 210). May or may not have a barbel......................... *Parexoglossum*

TONGUETIED MINNOW, *Parexoglossum laurae* Hubbs. Similar to the cutlips minnow. Kanawha River drainage of Virginia, West Virginia, and North Carolina.

Figure 210   Figure 211

**14a. Lower lip with fleshy side lobes; mouth sucker-like (Fig. 211)....
....** *Phenacobius*

SUCKERMOUTH MINNOW, *Phenacobius mirabilis* (Girard). Fig. 212. Pale olivaceous with a lateral band; black spot at base of caudal fin; breast naked; teeth 4-4. Length 4 inches. Colorado and South Dakota to western Ohio, Louisiana and Texas.

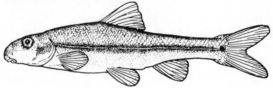

Figure 212

Phenacobius teretulus Cope. Fig. 213.. Without a distinct caudal spot and with a scaly breast. Kanawha River drainage in Virginia and West Virginia.

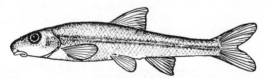

Figure 213

Phenacobius uranops Cope. Fig. 214. Breast and belly naked. Upper Tennessee River drainage.

Figure 214

87

14b. Lower lip without fleshy side lobes; mouth not sucker-like....15

15a. Barbel present on side or tip of maxillary; may be large but often minute and occasionally undeveloped in some individuals. 16

15b. Barbel absent from maxillary.................................21

16a. Barbel a short distance in front of end of maxillary and often concealed in groove between maxillary and premaxillary (Fig. 215). 17

Barbel in front of end of maxillary

Figure 215

16b. Barbel located at posterior end of maxillary (Fig. 216).....................18

Barbel at end of maxillary

Figure 216

17a. Upper jaw reaches to or behind front of eye; lateral line scales less than 60; dark silvery color......................*Semotilus*

CREEK CHUB, *Semotilus atromaculatus* (Mitchill). Fig. 217. Bluish above, light below; adults with black spot at anterior base of dorsal fin. Spring males rosy on sides. Teeth 2, 5-4, 2. Length up to 10 inches. Montana to eastern Canada and south to the Gulf.

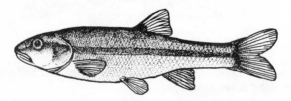

Figure 217

FALLFISH, *Semotilus corporalis* (Mitchill). Fig. 218. Similar to the creek chub, but lacks black spot in dorsal fin. Eastern Canada into James Bay drainage and south on east side of Appalachians to Virginia.

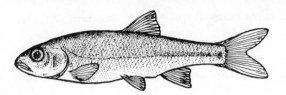

Figure 218

17b. Upper jaw does not reach to eye; lateral line scales more than 60; color dark and sometimes blotched .... *Semotilus*
PEARL DACE, *Semotilus margarita* (Cope). Fig. 219. Dusky mottled above or partly on sides, silvery below. Reddish in spring males. Teeth 2, 5-4, 2. Length 4 inches. Subspecies *S. m. margarita* (Cope), eastern Great Lakes drainage and Vermont to Virginia east of the Alleghenies and *S. m. nachtriebi* (Cox), northern states from the Rockies to New York.

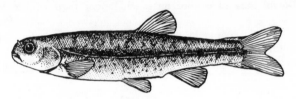

Figure 219

18a. Lateral line scales more than 70 .... **19**

18b. Lateral line scales less than 70 .... **20**

19a. Maxillary does not reach eye; teeth in two rows ...... *Mylocheilus*
COLUMBIA RIVER CHUB, *Mylocheilus caurinus* (Richardson). Fig. 220. Dark above, silvery on sides with dark lateral band below which is a shorter dark band. Males are reddish on belly and sides. Teeth (1) 2, 5-5, 2 (1). Length over 12 inches. Lower Columbia River drainage.

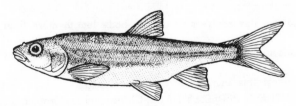

Figure 220

19b. Maxillary reaches eye; teeth in one row...............*Agosia*
LONGFIN DACE, *Agosia chrysogaster* Girard. Fig. 221. Similar to *Rhinichthys* but with a slight frenum hidden in the groove of premaxillary which is easily overlooked. Dark above, pale below with lateral band; male may have orange sides. Teeth 4-4. Length 4 inches. Lower Colorado River drainage.

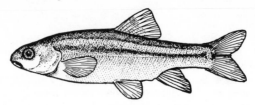

Figure 221

20a. Dorsal lobe of caudal fin much longer than ventral lobe.......
....*Pogonichthys*
SPLITTAIL, *Pogonichthys macrolepidotus* (Ayres). Fig. 222. Silvery; rudimentary rays of caudal fin very well developed. Teeth 2, (5)4-5, 2. Length over 12 inches. Sacramento River system of California.

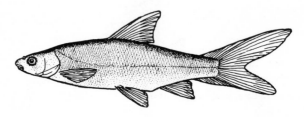

Figure 222

20b. Dorsal lobe of caudal not longer than ventral lobe...........
....CHUBS, *Hybopsis*
Many species, mostly east of the Rockies in this genus. For key to species see page 105.

21a. Lateral line scales or scales in body length more than 45.....**22**

21b. Lateral line scales or scales in body length less than 45.....**30**

22a. Lateral line incomplete or undeveloped.............*Chrosomus*
SOUTHERN REDBELLY DACE, *Chrosomus erythrogaster* Rafinesque. Fig. 223. Olive brown to blackish above and light below; two lateral dark bands with reddish streak between; scale rows about 85. Males

with reddish bellies. Length about 3 inches. Southern Minnesota to Pennsylvania and south to northern Alabama.

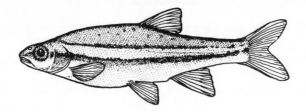

Figure 223

NORTHERN REDBELLY DACE, *Chrosomus eos* Cope. Similar to *C. erythrogaster* except snout shorter and mouth more oblique. Length up to 3 inches. Northern British Columbia to Hudson Bay drainage to New Brunswick and south to central Minnesota.

EASTERN REDBELLY DACE, *Chrosomus oreas* Cope. Fig. 224. Brightly colored with upper lateral band mostly posterior to anus. Length 3 inches. Upper James, Roanoke, and Kanawha Rivers.

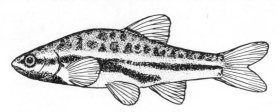

Figure 224

FINESCALE DACE, *Chrosomus neogaeus* (Cope). Fig. 225. Dark above and light below with dark lateral band above which is a light streak; more than 90 scale rows. Length up to 5 inches. Northwestern Canada to New England and south to northern Minnesota, Wisconsin and Michigan. Isolated populations in western Nebraska and in Black Hills.

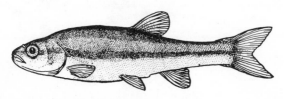

Figure 225

22b. Lateral line complete......................................23

23a. Pharyngeal teeth in one row, 4-5, 5-5, 5-4, or 6-6..............24

23b. Pharyngeal teeth in 2 rows,2 ,4(5)-(4)5, 2.....................28

24a. Anal fin rays 10 or more..................................25

24b. Anal fin rays usually less than 10.........................26

25a. Belly behind pelvic fins with a sharp naked keel; length of intestine about twice length of body................*Notemigonus*

GOLDEN SHINER, *Notemigonus crysoleucas* (Mitchill). Fig. 226. Body deep; silvery gold color; lateral line deeply decurved. Teeth 4-4 or 5-5. Length up to 10 inches. Many subspecies, Manitoba to Quebec and southward to Florida and Mexico. Introduced west of Rockies.

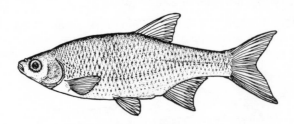

Figure 226

25b. Belly behind pelvic fins not with sharp naked keel; length of intestine more than twice length of body................*Lavinia*

HITCH, *Lavinia exilicauda* Baird and Girard. Fig. 227. Deep bodied; dark above, light below; mouth short, not extending much behind nostrils; lateral line deeply decurved. Teeth 4(5)-5. Length up to 12 inches. Several subspecies in streams of central California.

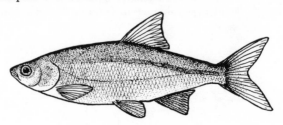

Figure 227

26a. Scales before dorsal fin 44-51; spot on base of caudal fin rays; sides more or less blotched..........................*Moapa*

DESERT MINNOW, *Moapa coriacea* Hubbs and Miller. Fig. 228. Deep olive above with blotches on sides and white on belly; sides marked with a golden brown lateral band above which is a light streak. Premaxillary is actually non-protractile, but the frenum connecting it is slight and hidden in the groove. Teeth usually 5-4. Resembles *Gila* and *Rhinichthys* but has only one row of pharyngeal teeth and lacks barbel. Length 2 inches. Moapa River, Nevada.

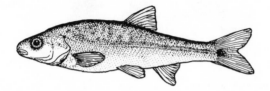

Figure 228

26b. Scales before dorsal fin less than 40; no distinct spot on base of caudal fin rays; sides not greatly blotched, if any..........27

27a. Front of dorsal fin well behind front of pelvic fins; 32-38 scales before dorsal fin................................*Hesperoleucas*

WESTERN ROACH, *Hesperoleucas symmetricus* (Baird and Girard) Fig. 229. Dusky above, pale below with a partial lateral band. Teeth 5-4. Length 5 inches Several subspecies, central and northern California.

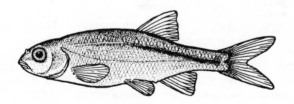

Figure 229

27b. Front of dorsal fin about over front of pelvic fins; 26-33 scales before dorsal fin......................................*Siphateles*

TUICHUB, *Siphateles bicolor* (Girard). Fig. 230. Olivaceous on back, lighter below with a dusky lateral band. Teeth 5-5, sometimes 2, 5-5, 2. Length 7-8 inches. Many subspecies, Columbia River in

Oregon to the Sacramento River in California and in isolated parts of the Lahontan basin of Nevada.

MOHAVE CHUB, *Siphateles mohavensis* Snyder. Mohave River, California.

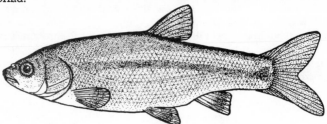

Figure 230

28a. Skin texture leathery.............................*Snyderichthys*
LEATHERSIDE CHUB, *Snyderichthys copei* (Jordan and Gilbert). Fig. 231. Body rather long and slender; bluish above, silvery below with a dusky lateral streak; origin of dorsal fin behind origin of pelvic fins; lateral line scales 80. Teeth 2, 5-4, 2. Length 6 inches. Bonneville and Snake River drainages of Nevada Utah, and Wyoming.

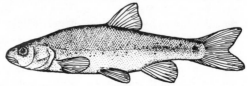

Figure 231

28b. Skin texture not very leathery.............................29

29a. Pharyngeal teeth far apart and scarcely hooked...*Ptychocheilus*
SQUAWFISH, *Ptychocheilus oregonensis* (Richardson). Fig. 232.
Dusky green above, silvery below; lateral line scales 67-75; 46-56 scales before dorsal fin; dorsal rays 9-10; anal rays 8. Teeth 2, 4-5, 2. Length up to 2 feet. Widespread in Columbia River drainage and in coastal streams of Oregon and Washington.

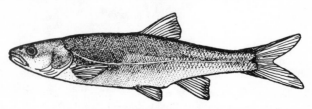

Figure 232

SACRAMENTO SQUAWFISH, *Ptychocheilus grandis* (Ayres). Fig. 233. Dark above, light below; lateral line scales 90-95; 36-41 scales before dorsal fin; dorsal rays 9; anal rays 7. Teeth 2, 5-4, 2. Length 20 inches. Lower Sacramento River drainage, California.

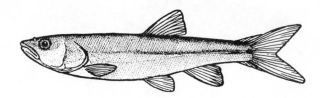

Figure 233

COLORADO SQUAWFISH, *Ptychocheilus lucius* Girard. Dark above and light below; lateral line scales 83-87; dorsal rays 9; anal rays 9. Teeth 2, 4-5, 2. Length nearly 5 feet; largest of all American ninnows. Lower Colorado River drainage.

Ptychocheilus umpquae Snyder. Similar to squawfish. Sinslaw and Umpquae Rivers, Oregon.

29b. Pharyngeal teeth close together and strongly hooked......*Gila**

REDSIDE DACE, *Gila elongata* (Kirtland). Fig. 234. Dusky blue above, sides and belly silvery (reddish in spring males); lateral band present; 65-70 lateral line scales; dorsal rays about 8; anal rays 9. Teeth 2, 4-5, 2. Length 5 inches. Southern Minnesota through part of the eastern Great Lakes and Ohio River drainages south to northeastern Oklahoma.

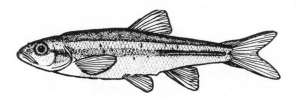

Figure 234

ROSY DACE, *Gila vandoisula* (Valenciennes). Fig. 235. Bluish green somewhat mottled above, pale below (reddish in spring males);

---

*The species formerly in the genera *Clinostomus* and *Richardsonius* are placed in this genus at the suggestion of Dr. Reeve M. Bailey.

48-53 lateral line scales; usually 9 dorsal rays; 8 anal rays. Teeth 2, 5-5(4), 2. Length 5 inches. Headwaters of streams from Chesapeake Bay to North Carolina.

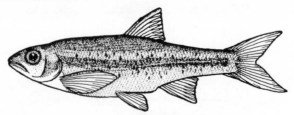

Figure 235

REDSIDE SHINER, *Gila balteata* (Richardson). Fig. 236. Dark above with silvery sides and belly, (rosy in spring males); 9-11 dorsal rays; more than 10 (16 or more) anal rays. Teeth 2, 5-4, 2. Length 6 inches. Subspecies in the Columbia River drainage and Salt Lake Basin.

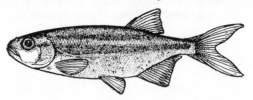

Figure 236

REDSIDE MINNOW, *Gila egregia* (Girard). Fig. 237. Very dark on back with golden belly (red in spring males); sides marked with 2 dark lateral bands with reddish streak between; about 8 dorsal rays; 9 anal rays. Teeth 2, 4-5, 2. Length 4 inches. Lahontan Basin and related waters of Nevada and California.

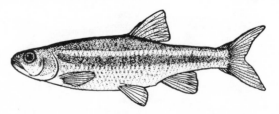

Figure 237

BONYTAIL CHUB, *Gila robusta* Baird and Girard. Fig. 238. Dusky above, pale below; origin of dorsal fin slightly behind origin of pelvic fins; dorsal rays 9; anal rays 9-11; lateral line scales 75-85. Teeth 2, (4)5-5(4), 2. Length 12-15 inches. Several subspecies in the Colorado

River drainage. *G. robusta elegans* Baird and Girard, mostly in main channel of Colorado River, has a very slender caudal peduncle and enlarged basal fulcra.

Gila cypha Miller. Has a humped back; uncertain specific status. Colorado River drainage.

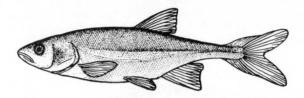

Figure 238

RIO GRANDE CHUB, *Gila nigrescens* (Girard). Fig. 239. Dusky above, silvery below; origin of dorsal fin behind the origin of the pelvic fins; dorsal rays 8; lateral line scales 55-70; basal fulcra of caudal fin not greatly enlarged. Teeth 2, 5-4, 2. Length 6-12 inches. Rio Grande River drainage of Colorado, New Mexico and Texas. Introduced into the lower Colorado River.

Figure 239

UTAH CHUB, *Gila atraria* (Girard). Fig. 240. Origin of dorsal fin over origin of pelvic fins; dorsal rays 9; anal rays 8; lateral line scales 51-63; basal fulcra of caudal fin not enlarged. Length 12-15 inches. Native to Bonneville drainage, Nevada, but introduced into other western streams.

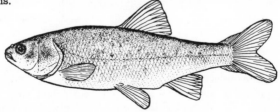

Figure 240

THICKTAIL CHUB, *Gila crassicauda* (Baird and Girard). Olivaceous above, pale below; origin of dorsal fin above origin of pelvic fins; dorsal rays 8; anal rays 8; lateral line scales 50-56. Teeth 2, 5-4, 2. Length 12 inches. Sacramento River, California.

BLUE CHUB, *Gila bicolor* (Girard). Fig. 241. Bluish above, silvery below; origin of dorsal fin over origin of pelvic fins; dorsal rays 8; anal rays 7-9; lateral line scales about 60-70; basal fulcra of caudal fin not enlarged. Teeth 2, 5-5, 2. Length 12 inches. Klamath Lake drainage, Oregon and California.

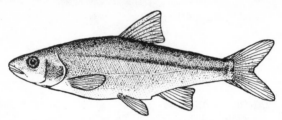

Figure 241

Other forms in isolated waters are the NEVADA BONY TAIL CHUB, *Gila jordani* Tanner, closely resembling the bony tail chub, Lincoln County, Nevada; the southern California chub, *Gila orcutti* (Eigenmann and Eigenmann), coastal streams of southern California from Santa Ynez to San Luis Rey, California; *Gila ditaena* Miller, extreme southern Arizona into Mexico; and *Gila pupurea* (Girard) known only from San Bernardino Creek Cochise Co., Arizona.

TUI CHUB, *Siphateles bicolor* (Girard). Individuals with pharyngeal teeth 2, 5-5, 2 will key here. (See Fig. 230, couplet 27b.)
30a. First rudimentary dorsal ray is more or less thickened and distinctly separated from the first well-developed ray by a membrane (Fig. 242) ....*Pimephales*

Scales anterior to the dorsal are more or less small and crowded. Breeding males are highly modified, and in some species males guard the eggs.

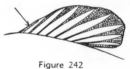

Figure 242

FATHEAD MINNOW, *Pimephales promelas* Rafinesque. Fig. 243.
Lateral line more or less incomplete; olivaceous. Adults have a horizontal dark bar across the dorsal fin nearly half way up. Lacks a caudal spot. Spring males (Fig. 244) are very dark and develop a heavy pad on their backs. Teeth 4-4. Length 2½ inches. Several

subspecies, widespread from southern Canada east of the Rockies to Maine and southward to the Susquehanna and to the Gulf States. Introduced west of the Rockies.

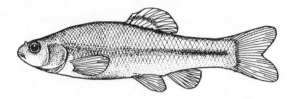

Figure 243

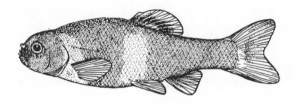

Figure 244

BLUNTNOSE MINNOW, *Pimephales notatus* (Rafinesque). Fig. 245. Lateral line complete; mouth inferior; olivaceous with dusky lateral band; black spot at the base of the front of the dorsal fin, and a prominent spot at the base of the caudal fin. Teeth 4-4. Length 4 inches. Widespread from North Dakota through the Great Lakes and southward.

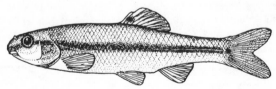

Figure 245

BULLHEAD MINNOW, *Pimephales vigilax* (Baird and Girard), Fig. 246. Dusky yellowish above, silvery below with dark lateral band; dark spot on the first four dorsal rays and a tiny spot at the base of caudal fin. Teeth 4-4. Length 3 inches. Differs in having shorter intestine and silvery instead of black peritoneum.

Several subspecies from Minnesota and West Virginia to northern Alabama and Texas.

P. vigilax vigilax (Baird and Girard) in the Red River system of Texas and Oklahoma and in the Brazos and San Jacinto River drainages of Texas.

P. vigilax perspicuus (Girard). Widespread from southern Minnesota to West Virginia and to northern Alabama and Oklahoma.

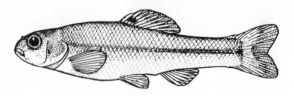

Figure 246

NEOSHO MOUNTAIN MINNOW, *Pimephales tenellus* (Girard) Fig. 247. Very similar and closely related to the bullhead minnow. Distinctly pigmented at base of anal fin and on ventral surface of caudal peduncle. Neosho River system of Oklahoma, Kansas and Missouri.

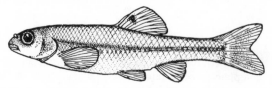

Figure 247

CASTOR MINNOW, *Pimephales callarchus* (Hubbs and Black). Similar to the Neohso Mountain minnow except it has a "V" shaped pattern about the anus. Castor River, Bollinger County, Missouri.

30b. First rudimentary dorsal ray is a thin splint closely attached to the first well-developed ray (Fig. 248)...........31

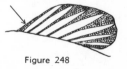

Figure 248

31a. Dorsal rays usually 9; mouth small and upturned so that it is almost vertical ....*Opsopoeodus*

PUGNOSE MINNOW, *Opsopoeodus emiliae* Hay. Fig. 249. Yellowish to silver with dark lateral band; breast scaleless. Teeth 5-5.

Length 2½ inches. Southern Minnesota to Michigan and south to Florida and Texas.

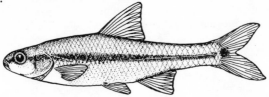

Figure 249

31b. Dorsal rays usually 8 or less; mouth normal size, may be oblique or horizontal, except in *N. anogenus* where it is almost vertical. . 32

32a. Mandible, maxillary, suborbitals and subopercle with visible cavernous chambers .... *Ericymba*

Figure 250

SILVERJAW MINNOW, *Ericymba buccata* Cope. Fig. 250. Olivaceous above with silvery sides and belly. Teeth 1, 4-4, 0. Length 4-5 inches. Distributed from southeastern Missouri to western Pennsylvania and south to Florida and Arkansas.

32b. Mandible, maxillary, suborbitals and subopercles without visible cavernous chambers. 33

33a. Inner row of teeth 4-5 or 5-4..............................**34**

33b. Inner row of teeth 4-4....................................**35**

34a. Lateral line completely absent......................*Iotichthys*

PIGMY MINNOW, *Iotichthys phlegethontis* (Cope). Fig. 251. Olivaceous with broad lateral band and light below. Teeth 1, 5-4, 2. Small, about 1½ inches long. Tributaries of Great Salt Lake and Lake Sevier, Utah.

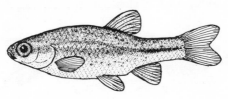

Figure 251

34b. Lateral line present but incomplete (about halfway)...*Hemitrema*
FLAME DACE, *Hemitrema flammea* (Jordan and Gilbert). Fig. 252.
Dark on back, pale below with dark lateral band above which is a
light streak. Spring males with red belly. Teeth 2, 4-5, 2. Length 2½
inches. Tributaries of upper Tennessee River in Tennessee and northern Alabama.

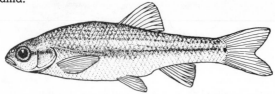

Figure 252

**35a. Intestine short "S" shape, less than twice the standard length;
peritoneum usually silvery or speckled......SHINERS, *Notropis***
Contains more species than any other genus of freshwater fishes.
For key to species see page 113.

**35b. Intestine longer, coiled more or less spring-like and more than
twice the standard length; peritoneum black.................36**

**36a. Body with dark lateral band; mouth "U" shape; suborbitals very
narrow, little wider than infraorbital canal..............*Dionda***
OZARK MINNOW, *Dionda nubila* (Forbes). Fig. 253. Body dark
with dark lateral band around snout, through eye, and on sides to
faint caudal spot. Length 2½ inches. Wyoming to Illinois and south to
Ozarks.

Figure 253

ROUNDNOSE MINNOW, *Dionda episcopa* Girard. Fig. 254. Similar
to the Ozark minnow except the snout is blunter and the mouth is
smaller. Several subspecies. Oklahoma through Texas into Mexico.

Figure 254

36b. Body silvery or yellowish without a well developed lateral band; mouth gently curved, crescent shape; suborbittals broad, reaching nearly halfway across cheek......................*Hybognathus*

NORTHERN PLAINS MINNOW, *Hybognathus placita* Girard. Fig. 255. Silvery color, scales with few strong radii; eye small, 5 x in head; mouth smaller than in silvery minnow and more inferior; head elongate. Length 6 inches. Upper Missouri drainage and southward, Currently considered as a form of the silvery minnow by Dr. R. M. Bailey.

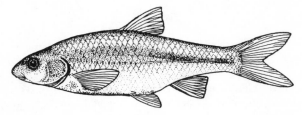

Figure 255

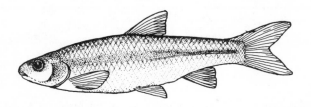

Figure 256

SILVERY MINNOW, *Hybognathus nuchalis* Agassiz. Fig. 256. Silvery color with dark back; scales with about 10 radii (Fig. 257); eye large, 4 to 4.5 x in head; head elongate. Length 6 inches. Several subspecies ranging from the Missouri drainage of Montana to Lake Champlain and south to the Gulf.

Figure 257

CYPRESS MINNOW, *Hybognathus hayi* Jordan. Fig. 258. Silvery color with dark back, similar to silvery minnow except body more slender and snout shorter. Scales with about 10 strong radii. **Length**

3-4 inches. Ranges from southern Indiana southward to Tennessee and Mississippi.

Figure 258

BRASSY MINNOW, *Hybognathus hankinsoni* Hubbs. Fig. 259. Color yellowish; similar to silvery minnow; scales with about 20 faint radii (Fig. 260); head blunt. Length 3-4 inches. Ranges from Montana to Lake Champlain and southward to Nebraska, Missouri and Colorado.

Figure 260

Figure 259

37a. **Scales present although minute; desert minnows....***Lepidomeda*
WHITE RIVER SPINEDACE, *Lepidomeda vittata* Cope. Fig. 261. Olivaceous above, silvery below with lateral band; eye 3¾ x in head; depth 4¼ x in length. Teeth 2, 4-4, 2. Length 3 inches. Desert streams of Nevada and Utah.

Lepidomeda jarrovi Cope. Similar to White River spinedace, but has a larger eye, 3¼ x in head; depth 5 x in length. Desert streams of Arizona and Nevada.

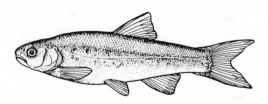

Figure 261

37b. Scales absent; desert minnows...........................**38**

38a. Barbel present on maxillary........................*Plagopterus*
   SILVER DACE, *Plagopterus argentissimus* Cope. Fig. 262. Dusky back, silvery below. Teeth 2, 5-4, 2. Length 2½ inches. Gila River, Arizona. Known at present only from the Virgin River system of Arizona, Utah and Nevada.

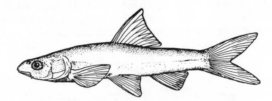

Figure 262

38b. Barbel absent from maxillary...........................*Meda*
   DESERT MINNOW, *Meda fulgida* Girard, Fig. 263. Dusky above, silvery on sides and below; somewhat speckled. Teeth 2, 5-5, 2. Length 3 inches. Gila River, Arizona.

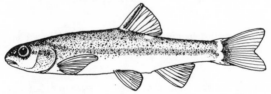

Figure 263

CHUBS, Genus *Hybopsis*

1a. Snout not bulging forward or extending to any appreciable distance beyond upper lip (Fig. 264); mouth more or less terminal..2

 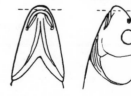

Figure 264   Figure 265

1b. Snout bulging or distinctly extending beyond upper lip (Fig. 265);
mouth distinctly subterminal....................................6

2a. Scales small, lateral line scales more than 50. Fig. 266.......
.................NORTHERN CHUB, *Hybopsis plumbea* (Agassiz)
Dusky color with a rather obscure lateral band. Barbel slightly
anterior to end of maxillary. Teeth 2, 4-4, 2. Length up to 6 inches.
Mackenzie River basin, most of Great Lakes, Hudson River and Delaware River drainages. Represented by subspecies west of Lake Superior and in the upper Missouri River drainage; also in Lake Pend
d'Oreille, Idaho and in the Fraser River.

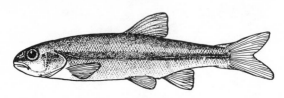

Figure 266

2b. Scales larger, 50 or less in the lateral line.....................3

3a. Snout about equal to diameter of eye; caudal spot mostly on rays
of caudal fin..4

3b. Snout much longer than diameter of eye; caudal spot mostly on
peduncle at base of caudal fin...............................5

4a. Body deep; caudal spot faint. Fig. 267.......................
.....................OREGON CHUB, *Hybopsis crameri* Snyder
Somewhat speckled or mottled; barbel minute and sometimes
poorly developed. Length about 2 inches. Willamette and Umpqua
Rivers, Oregon.

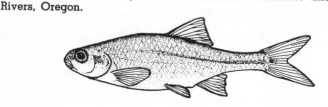

Figure 267

106

4b. Body slender; caudal spot black. Fig. 268.....................
....................FLORIDA CHUB, *Hybopsis harperi* (Fowler)

Silvery below with dark lateral band above which is a light streak, and with a dark back. Length about 2 inches. Northern Florida and adjacent regions of Georgia and Alabama.

Figure 268

5a. Spot at base of caudal fin round and rather dark; distance from front of eye to tip of snout goes 2 or more times in distance from front of eye to hind margin of opercle. Teeth 1, 4-4, 1, (0). Fig. 269.
...............HORNYHEAD CHUB, *Hybopsis biguttata* (Kirtland)

Dark olive above, pale below. Young individuals have more distinct lateral band and caudal spot. Length 8-10 inches. Wyoming and North Dakota to the Hudson River and south to northeastern Oklahoma and northern Ohio River drainage.

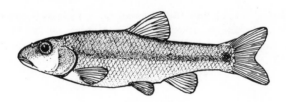

Figure 269

5b. Caudal spot smaller and rather pale, not always round; distance from tip of snout to front margin of eye goes 2 or less times in distance from front of eye to hind margin of opercle. Teeth 4-4. Fig. 270..............RIVER CHUB, *Hybopsis micropogon* (Cope)

Dark olive above, pale below. Length 6 to 9 inches. Wabash River to Michigan and western New York and south to Virginia and on west side of Appalachians to northern Georgia and Alabama.

Several closely related species occur south of this range. EASTERN PIEDMONT CHUB, *Hybopsis leptocephala* (Girard) with a shorter and more rounded snout occurs in the streams from the James River in Virginia southward. A similar but undescribed chub occurs in the headwaters of the New and Roanoke Rivers in Virginia.

The SOUTHERN CHUB, *Hybopsis bellica* (Girard). Similar to eastern Piedmont chub. Southernmost representative of this group; Savannah River, Georgia westward in the Gulf drainage to Louisiana.

Figure 270

6a. Body irregularly speckled with black spots or small blotches, or with 8 to 11 blotches on a dusky lateral band..................7

6b. Body not speckled and with no blotches along lateral line.....12

7a. Upper lobe of caudal fin light, lower lobe with dark pigment and light margin...8

7b. Both lobes of caudal fin light or only faintly pigmented at base..9

8a. Scales of lateral line 40-43; dorsal fin not pointed; sides speckled; each scale above lateral line with a strong ridge. Fig. 271......
....................STURGEON CHUB, *Hybopsis gelida* (Girard)
Dusky above and silvery below; barbel short but distinct; eye small. Teeth 4-4. Length about 3 inches. Missouri River drainage.

Figure 271

8b. Scales of lateral line 46-50; dorsal fin very pointed; sides not speckled; scales without ridges. Fig. 272........................
.........SICKLEFIN CHUB, *Hybopsis meeki* Jordan and Evermann
Silvery with dusky lateral band and faint caudal spot. All fins very large, the pectoral reaching far past the base of the pelvic fins;

barbel long; eye small. Teeth 4-4. Length 2 inches. Missouri River drainage.

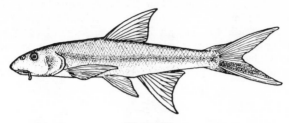

Figure 272

9a. Blotches present on sides along lateral band..................10

9b. Blotches not present on sides along lateral band..............11

10a. Scales in lateral line 46-49. Fig. 273.........................
.................**SPOTTED CHUB, Hybopsis dissimilis (Kirtland)**
Olivaceous above and light below with a pale bluish lateral band and a caudal spot; slightly speckled sometimes above lateral line; head rather broad. Teeth 4-4. Length 4 inches. Iowa and the Ohio River drainage north of the Ohio River to Oklahoma. Includes form called *H. wautaga* Jordan and Evermann (Fig. 274) in the upper Tennessee River drainage which is now considered the same species.

Figure 273

Figure 274

10b. Scales in lateral line 40-49...................................
........**BLOTCHED CHUB, Hybopsis insignis Hubbs and Crowe**
Sides with row of dark blotches (large as pupil) and with scattered specks; mid-dorsal row of blotches present. Teeth 4-4. Length 3 inches. Cumberland and Tennessee River systems.

11a. Barbel as long or longer than pupil of eye; sides of body rather heavily sprinkled with black dots. Fig. 275.....................
....................SPECKLED CHUB, *Hybopsis aestivalis* (Girard)
Silvery and more or less heavily speckled; anal rays usually 8; belly naked. Teeth 4-4. Length 2½ inches. Several subspecies ranging from upper Missouri River drainage to the Rio Grande. *H. a. tetranema* Gilbert (Fig. 276) with two pairs of barbels occurs in the Arkansas River drainage of Oklahoma, Arkansas and Kansas.

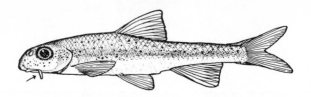

Figure 275

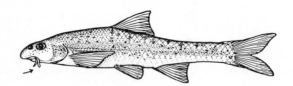

Figure 276

11b. Barbel shorter than pupil of eye; sides and back marked with scattered "X" shaped spots. Fig. 277...........................
.........GRAVEL CHUB, *Hybopsis x-punctata* Hubbs and Crowe
Silvery with no distinct spots on pale lateral band; anal rays usually 7. Belly scaled. Teeth 4-4. Length about 4 inches. Southern Minnesota to Ohio and to Oklahoma.

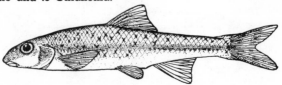

Figure 277

12a. Lateral line scales usually more than 50; occasionally some individuals may have as few as 48..........................13

12b. Lateral line scales less than 50, usually less than 48.........14

13a. Dorsal fin distinctly falcate; no spot at base of caudal fin. Fig. 278.
.......**PLAINS FLATHEAD CHUB,** *Hybopsis gracilis* **(Richardson)**
Pale olive above and silvery below; barbel rather long; head broad, width equal to depth; mouth large, reaching past front of eye. Teeth 2, 4-4, 2. Length up to 12 inches. Several subspecies in streams of the plains from Saskatchewan south to Oklahoma.

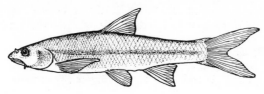

Figure 278

13b. Dorsal fin not falcate; a dark caudal spot present. Fig. 279......
....................**SPOTFIN CHUB,** *Hybopsis monacha* **(Cope)**
Light olive above, silvery below; black blotch in upper part of dorsal fin; barbel small; head not broad; mouth small, not reaching past eye. Teeth 4-4. Length about 4 inches. Upper Tennessee River drainage.

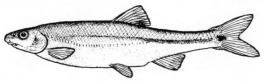

Figure 279

14a. Dorsal fin with spot in upper posterior portion. Fig. 280......
....................**THICKLIP CHUB,** *Hybopsis labrosa* **(Cope)**
Snout long and blunt; barbels very long; small spot at base of caudal fin. Males are steel blue with black markings on back, especially at base of caudal fin. Females are pale silvery with bluish streak on caudal peduncle. Teeth 1, 4-4, 1. Length 3 inches. Santee River drainage, North and South Carolina.

Figure 280

14b. Dorsal fin without spot....................................15

15a. Front of dorsal fin above or behind front of pelvic fin; pigment present at base of anal fin................................16

15b. Front of dorsal fin more or less before front of pelvic fins; no pigment at base of anal fin.............................17

16a. Caudal spot present..**FLORIDA CHUB**, *Hybopsis harperi* (Fowler)
(See Fig. 268, couplet 4b.) Individuals with overhanging snout will key here.

SLENDER CHUB, *Hybopsis cahni* Hubbs and Crowe. Dusky above, light below; body slender and with long slender peduncle. Teeth 4-4. Length 2½ inches. Powell and Clinch Rivers, Tennessee.

16b. Caudal spot absent. Fig. 281..................................
..................**BIGEYE CHUB**, *Hybopsis amblops* (Rafinesque)
Dusky green above and silvery below with a prominent silvery lateral band which is often heavily pigmented. Teeth 1, 4-4, 1. Length 2-3 inches. New York to Iowa and south to western Florida, Louisiana, and northeastern Oklahoma.

Hybopsis rubrifrons (Jordan). Similar to bigeye chub except the head is longer and narrower. Altamaha River system, Georgia.

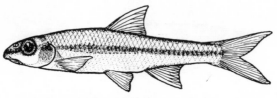

Figure 281

17a. Eye Small, 3¾ times in head length; dorsal fin not falcate. Fig. 282..............**HIGHBACK CHUB**, *Hybopsis hypsinota* (Cope)
Silvery with dusky lateral band passing around snout; faint caudal spot present. Males are deep violet luster with pink fins. Teeth 1, 4-4, 1. Length 3 inches. Santee River drainage, North and South Carolina.

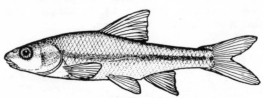

Figure 282

17b. Eye large, 3 to 3 1/3 times in head length; dorsal fin falcate. Fig. 283............SILVER CHUB, *Hybopsis storeriana* (Kirtland)
Pale greenish above and silvery below with a slight dusky band and no caudal spot. Teeth 1, 4-4, 1. Length up to 10 inches. Red River drainage of North Dakota to New York and south to northern Alabama and Oklahoma.

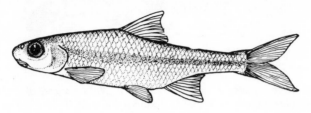

Figure 283

SHINERS, genus *Notropis*

1a. Body depth usually less than 5 times in length from snout to base of caudal fin*..2

1b. Body depth usually 5 times or more in length from snout to base of caudal fin..14

2a. Body depth usually less than 4 times in length from snout to base of caudal fin.. 3

2b. Body depth usually 4 to 5 times in length from snout to base of caudal fin 32

3a. Distinct spot present at base of caudal fin.....................4

3b. Spot not present or not distinct at base of caudal fin............9

4a. Spot at base of caudal fin large (approximately the size of the eye) and very black..5

4b. Spot at base of caudal fin small (usually much smaller than the eye) or rather faint..6

5a. Anal rays usually 7 to 8. Fig. 284...............................
...............BLACKTAIL SHINER, *Notropis venustus* (Girard)
Somewhat variable in parts of range. Includes those forms known as *N. notatus, N. stigmaturus, N. cercostigma,* etc. Olivaceous above and

*This is an unorthodox method for dividing this genus. Immature individuals and some subspecies may have greater or less body depth than that for adults or that characteristic for the species. Consequently, some species are keyed in several categories.

silvery below. Teeth 4-4. Length 5-6 inches. Southern Missouri to Texas and Florida. (See Fig. 355, couplet 57a.)

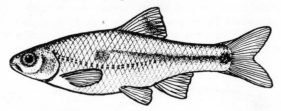

Figure 284

5b. Anal rays usually 9 to 11. Fig. 285....*Notropis zonistius* (Jordan)
Steel blue above, pale below; caudal fin with light spots at base; dorsal fin with horizontal bar; dark bar behind opercle. Teeth 2, 4-4, 2. Length 4 inches. Chattahoochee River drainage of Alabama and Georgia.

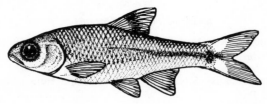

Figure 285

6a. Anal rays 7 to 8, usually 7....................................7

6b. Anal rays 9 to 11...8

7a. Scales before dorsal fin 12; maxillary reaching past eye; lower jaw slightly included. Fig. 286...............................
..**TAMAULIPAS SHINER,** *Notropis braytoni* Jordan and Evermann
Brownish with silvery lateral band. Teeth 4-4. Rio Grande drainage, Texas into Mexico.

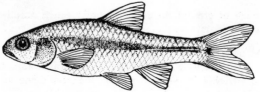

Figure 286

7b. Scales before dorsal fin 15-16; maxillary reaching to front of eye; lower jaw equal to upper.....................................
................**TOPEKA SHINER, Notropis topeka Gilbert. Fig. 287.**
Olivaceous with dusky lateral band. Teeth 4-4. Length 2¾ inches. South Dakota and southern Minnesota to Kansas and Missouri.

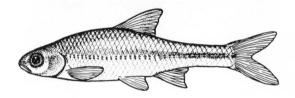

Figure 287

Notropis leedsi Fowler.
Bluish above; silvery below with broad dark lateral band ending in faint caudal spot; adults with blotch half way up on front of dorsal fin. Teeth 4-4. Length 2¾ inches. Savannah River to Ochlocknee River in Georgia and Florida.

8a. Basal part of caudal fin with pair of light spots. (See Fig. 285, couplet 5b.).........................**Notropis zonistius (Jordan)**
Dorsal fin about over pelvic fin. Young have smaller caudal spots and will key here.

HIGHFIN SHINER, Notropis altipinnis (Cope).............**Fig. 288**
Front of dorsal fin behind front of pelvic fin. Teeth 2, 4-4, 2. Many subspecies in coastal streams, Virginia to South Carolina.

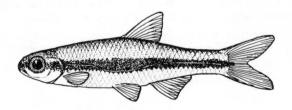

Figure 288

SAILFIN SHINER, Notropis hypselopterus (Gunther).......**Fig. 289**
Front of dorsal fin far behind front of pelvic fins; dorsal fin with blotch; caudal fin with 2 rosy spots at base; sides with wide silvery

lateral band. Teeth 1, 4-4, 1. Length 2½ inches. Western Florida into Louisiana.

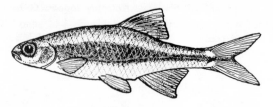

Figure 289

Notropis stonei Fowler...................................**Fig. 290**
Similar to sailfin shiner. Dusky above and pale below. Teeth 5-4. Length 1½ inches. South Carolina.

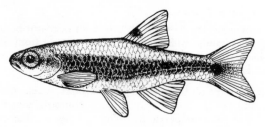

Figure 290

Notropis euryzonus Suttkus.
Similar to sailfin shiner, but differs in having a more rectangular dorsal fin (males) and in pigmentation. Teeth 2, 4-4, 2. Length 2¼ inches. Apalachicola River system, Georgia and Alabama.

FLAGFIN SHINER, *Notropis signipinnis* Bailey and Suttkus. .**Fig. 291**
Silvery with a very broad lateral band; base of caudal fin with 2 yellowish spots. Teeth 2, 4-4, 2. Length 2½ inches. Gulf drainage of Louisiana to western Florida.

Figure 291

116

8b. Basal part of caudal fin without a pair of light spots; fin marked
with crescent shape bands....................................
............FIRE SHINER, *Notropis pyrrhomelas* (Cope). **Fig. 292.**
Steel blue above and white below with scarlet bands on fins and
head. Teeth 1, 4-4, 1. Length 3¼ inches. Santee and Pedee River drainages in North and South Carolina.
Notropis xaenurus (Jordan).
May key here but caudal fin without crescent band. (See couplet
42a.)

Figure 292

9a. First dorsal ray longer than last ray when fin is depressed......
........COMMON SHINER, *Notropis cornutus* (Mitchill). **Fig. 293.**
Silvery with dusky dorsal band; no lateral band. Adults appear
to be rather loosely scaled. Teeth 2, 4-4, 2. Length 7-8 inches. Colorado eastward to Appalachians.

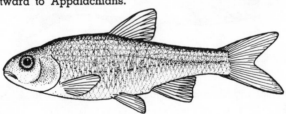

Figure 293

VIRGINIA SHINER, *Notropis cerasinus* (Cope)...........**Fig. 294**
Similar to common shiner except scales are deeper and some of
lateral scales are deeply pigmented. Teeth 2, 4-4, 2. Length 7 inches.
Upper Roanoke and Kanawha River drainages, Virginia and West Virginia.

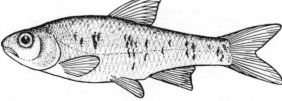

Figure 294

WHITE SHINER, *Notropis albeolus* Jordan................**Fig. 295**
Similar to common shiner except snout is sharper. Teeth 2, 4-4, 2. Length 7 inches. Coastal drainage of Roanoke River in Virginia southward and on west side of divide in West Virginia.

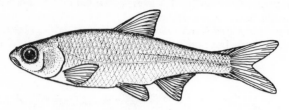

Figure 295

BLACKFIN SHINER, *Notropis bellus* (Hay)..............**Fig. 296**
Dusky silvery with dusky lateral band and with orange on belly and fin bases. Readily distinguished by deeply pigmented margins of fins. Teeth 2, 4-4, 2. Length 2½ inches. Gulf drainage of Alabama and Mississippi.

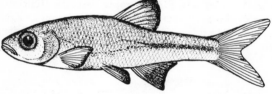

Figure 296

9b. First dorsal ray shorter than last ray when dorsal fin is depressed
....**10**

10a. Dorsal fin without blotch or pigment on any part. Fig. 297.....
............**RED SHINER, *Notropis lutrensis* (Baird and Girard)**
Steel blue above and silvery below. Males with orange on fins, belly and behind shoulders. Wyoming to southern Minnesota and Illinois and southward to Mexico. Teeth 4-4. Length 3 inches.

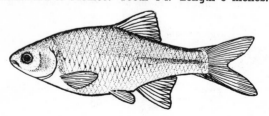

Figure 297

10b. Dorsal fin with blotch or pigmentation on either anterior or posterior base 11

11a. Anal rays usually 8. Fig. 298...............................
.................SPOTFIN SHINER, *Notropis spilopterus* (Cope)
Silvery with dark blotch on posterior part of dorsal fin. Teeth 1, 4-4, 1. Length 4 inches. North Dakota and Missouri to Lake Champlain and the Potomac River.

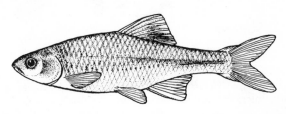

Figure 298

11b. Anal rays usually 9 to 11...............................12

12a. Dark blotch at base of anterior dorsal rays. Fig. 299.........
.................REDFIN SHINER, *Notropis umbratilis* (Girard)
Steel blue above and silvery below. Usually deep-bodied, but depth varies with age and subspecies. Teeth 2, 4-4, 2. Length 3 inches. Southern Minnesota and eastern Kansas eastward to Lake Ontario, in parts of Kentucky and West Virginia.

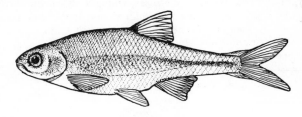

Figure 299

12b. No blotch at base of anterior rays, but a dark blotch between last dorsal rays...13

13a. Caudal fin with pair of light spots at base of caudal fin. Fig. 300.
.....BLUNTFACE SHINER, *Notropis camurus* (Jordan and Meek)

Silvery with caudal fin marked as in whitetail shiner. Teeth 1, 4-4, 1. Length 4 inches. Drainage of Arkansas River.

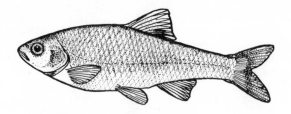

Figure 300

13b. Caudal fin with no light areas on base. Fig. 301..............
..............SATINFIN SHINER, *Notropis analostanus* (Girard)
Silvery color; lateral line scales 34-35. Teeth 1, 4-4, 1. Length 4 inches. Coastal drainage from the St. Lawrence to North Carolina.

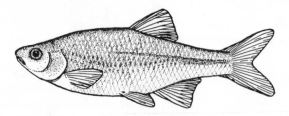

Figure 301

STEELCOLOR SHINER, *Notropis whipplei* (Girard).
Silvery color, very similar to spotfin shiner; lateral line scales 38-40. Teeth 1, 4-4, 1. Length 4 inches. Illinois through Ohio.
    Notropis trichroistius (Jordan and Gilbert)..............**Fig. 302**
Olivaceous with well-developed lateral band ending in elongated caudal spot. Dorsal fin dusky at base in front and on last rays. Length 2½ inches. Alabama River system.

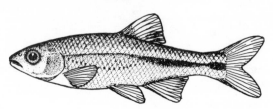

Figure 302

14a. Snout extending in a distinct bulge beyond upper lip..........15

14b. Snout not extending any appreciable distance before upper lip. 17

15a. Mouth distinctly oblique; spot present before base of caudal fin.
Fig. 303........MIRROR SHINER, *Notropis spectrunculus* (Cope)
Olivaceous above, silvery below with dusky band, fins dusky. Teeth
4-4. Length 3 inches. Headwaters of Tennessee River.

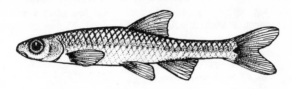

Figure 303

15b. Mouth not very oblique, but almost horizontal; no spot before
base of caudal fin.......................................16

16a. Lateral band dusky. Fig. 304.................................
....................OZARK SHINER, *Notropis ozarcanus* Meek.
Olivaceous with dusky lateral band. Teeth 4-4. Length 2½ inches.
Ozark streams of Missouri and Arkansas.

Figure 304

16b. Lateral band faint. Fig. 305.................................
...............LONGNOSE SHINER, *Notropis longirostris* (Hay)
Pale straw color with very faint lateral band; fins dusky. Teeth
1, 4-4, 1(0). Length 2½ inches. Coastal streams, eastern Louisiana to
southeastern Georgia and western Florida.

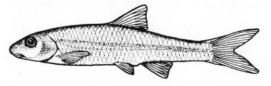

Figure 305

17a. Anal rays 7 to 8...18
17b. Anal rays usually 9 to 11...................................23
18a. Body depth scarcely over 5 (5.0 to about 5.2) times in body
length 19
18b. Body depth considerably over 5 (5.3 to over 6.0) times in body
length 21
19a. Lateral line very incomplete. Fig. 306......................
....................BRIDLED SHINER, *Notropis bifrenatus* (Cope)
Straw color with very black lateral band touching snout and chin.
Teeth 4-4. Length 2 inches. Atlantic drainage, Maine to Virginia.

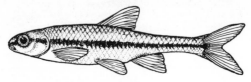

Figure 306

19b. Lateral line usually complete..............................20

20a. Scales before dorsal fin 10 to 12. MIMIC SHINER, *Notropis volucellus* (Cope)...Fig. 307
No spot before base of caudal fin; olivaceous with faint lateral
streak. Teeth 4-4. Length 2½ inches. Several subspecies from southern
Canada through Minnesota to Texas.

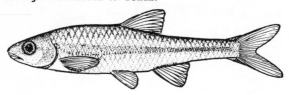

Figure 307

SWALLOWTAIL SHINER, *Notropis procne* (Cope).......Fig. 308
Olivaceous with dark lateral band; faint spot sometimes before
caudal fin; anal rays always 7. Teeth 4-4. Length 2½ inches. Delaware River to South Carolina.

Figure 308

122

20b. Scales before dorsal fin 14 to 18. **REDLIP SHINER,** *Notropis chiliticus* (Cope)..**Fig. 309**
Olivaceous with silvery lateral band. Males with red on head, especially on lips and on dorsal and anal fins. Teeth 2, 4-4, 2. Length 2 inches. Virginia and South Carolina.
   Notropis hypsilepis **Suttkus and Raney.**
   Lightly colored, silvery. Teeth 2, 4-4, 2. Length 2 inches. Very pale lateral band. Apalachicola River system, Alabama and Georgia.

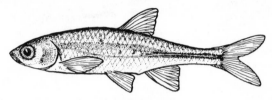

Figure 309

   Notropis xaenocephalus (Jordan)........................**Fig. 310**
Silvery with dark lateral band ending in a confluent caudal spot; lateral band passes through eye and touches chin. Teeth 2, 4-4, 2. Length 2 inches. Alabama River system, Alabama and Georgia.

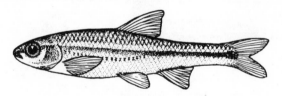

Figure 310

   GREENHEAD SHINER, *Notropis chlorocephalus* (Cope)....**Fig. 311**
Olivaceous dusted with black specks and dusky lateral band. Males with much red. Teeth 2, 4-4, 2. Length 2½ inches. North and South Carolina.

Figure 311

   Notropis stilbius **Jordan.**
   Pale green; silvery lateral band with specks anteriorly and at base of caudal fin. Teeth 2, 4-4, 1. Length 3 inches. Alabama River system.

NORTHERN WEED SHINER, *Notropis texanus richardsoni*, Hubbs and Greene ....Fig. 312
Slender form of *N. roseus*. (See couplet No. 58a.) Olivaceous above, silvery below. Males with fins rosy red. Teeth 2, 4-4, 2. Length 2½ inches. Minnesota and Michigan into Iowa and Illinois.

Figure 312

21a. Dorsal fin heavily pigmented and without spots or bars. TEN-NESSEE SHINER, *Notropis leuciodus* (Cope)..............Fig. 313
Olivaceous, silvery with dark lateral band; caudal spot continuous with lateral band. Teeth 2, 4-4, 2. Length 3 inches. Upper Tennessee River drainage.

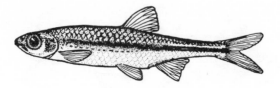

Figure 313

Notropis asperifrons Suttkus and Raney.................Fig. 314
Silvery with a distinct lateral band and caudal spot. Teeth 2, 4-4, 2. Length 2½ inches. Alabama and Black Warrior River systems, Alabama and Georgia.

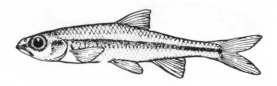

Figure 314

21b. Dorsal fin with slight but distinct pigmentation................22

22a. Lateral line more or less incomplete. Fig. 315.................
.................TAILLIGHT SHINER, *Notropis maculatus* (Hay)
Straw color, sometimes with reddish tinge and with very dark lateral and dorsal bands; dark streak on each side of anal base. Teeth 4-4. Length 2½ inches. Eastern Louisiana to southeastern Georgia and western Florida.

Figure 315

22b. Lateral line complete. (See Fig. 338, couplet 43a.).............
...............SNOWY SHINER, *Notropis niveus niveus* (Cope)
Pale with faint lateral band. Teeth 1, 4-4, 1. Length 2½ inches. Virginia to South Carolina. Some variation in subspecies.

23a. Lateral line incomplete, 2/3 body length. Fig. 316.............
..................RIBBON SHINER, *Notropis fumeus* Evermann
Yellowish and speckled with a dark lateral band. Teeth 2, 4-4, 2. Length 2 inches. Texas.

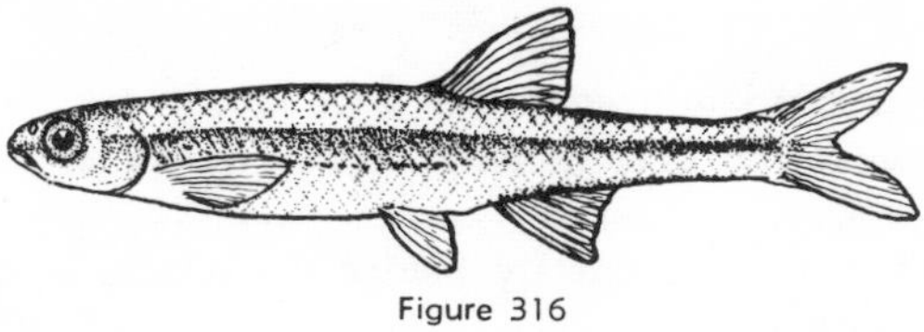

Figure 316

23b. Lateral line complete..24
24a. Scales in lateral line usually 40 or more. ROSEFIN SHINER, *Notropis ardens* (Cope)....................................Fig. 317
Steel blue above and light below with dark lateral band. Teeth 2, 4-4, 2. Length 3½ inches. Fins reddish in males. Several subspecies in Virginia (Roanoke River) and the upper and central Ohio River drainage.

Figure 317

Notropis roseipinnis Hay...............................Fig. 318
Dark above lateral line with dusky lateral band; black spot in middle of dorsal fin. Teeth 2, 4-4, 2. Length 2¼ inches. Coastal streams, Louisiana to Florida.

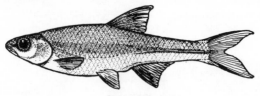

Figure 318

MOUNTAIN SHINER, *Notropis lirus* Jordan..............Fig. 319
Pale with dark lateral band through snout; spot in dorsal fin like that in *N. umbratilis.* Teeth 2, 4-4, 2. Length 2½ inches. Alabama River system.

Figure 319

24b. Scales in lateral line usually less than 40....................25
25a. Front of dorsal fin over or only slightly before or behind front of pelvic fins...26
25b. Front of dorsal fin completely behind the middle of the base of the pelvic fins..29
26a. First dorsal ray longer than last dorsal ray when fin is depressed 27
26b. First dorsal ray equal or shorter than last dorsal ray when fin is depressed...28
27a. Peritoneum silvery. KIAMICHI SHINER, *Notropis ortenburgeri* Hubbs ....Fig. 320
Pale with dusky lateral band extending through snout and chin. Length 2 inches. Oklahoma.

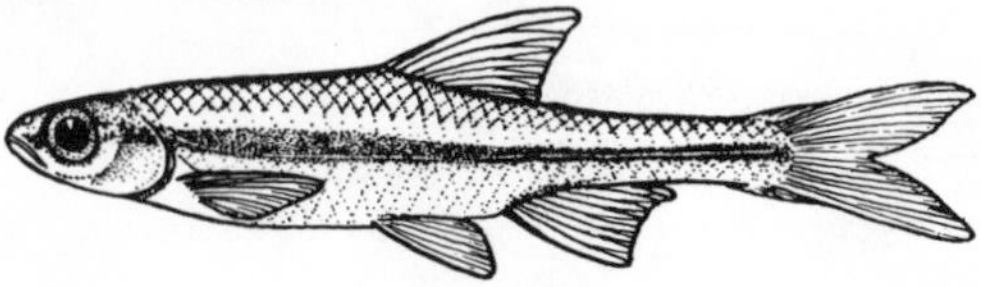

Figure 320

Notropis perpallidus Hubbs and Black.
Similar to Kiamichi shiner, but more pale and with faint lateral band. Teeth 2 (1), 4-4, 2 (1). Arkansas and eastern Oklahoma.

27b. **Peritoneum black. Fig. 321**....................................
............**POPEYE SHINER, *Notropis ariommus ariommus* (Cope)**
Scales dark edged above lateral line, pale below; eye very large. Teeth 2, 4-4, 2. Length 5 inches. Ohio River drainage.

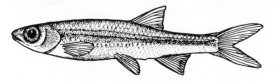

Figure 321

28a. **No pigment on body at base of anal fin. Fig. 322**.............
...................**SILVER SHINER, *Notropis photogenis* (Cope)**
Olivaceous with silvery lateral band and black dorsal stripe. Teeth 2, 4-4, 2. Length 4 inches. Most of Ohio River drainage.

Figure 322

28b. **Pigment on body at base of anal fin (thin line). Fig. 323**.......
...............**SHORTFIN SHINER, *Notropis micropteryx* (Cope)**
Olivaceous above and silvery below with dark lateral band. Teeth 2, 4-4, 2. Length 4 inches. Headwaters of Tennessee and Cumberland Rivers, also Ozark region of Missouri and Arkansas.

Figure 323

29a. Body pale; no pigment at base of anal fin. EMERALD SHINER,
Notropis atherinoides Rafinesque......................**Fig. 324**
 Pale with faint lateral band. Teeth 2, 4-4, 2. Length 4 inches. Several subspecies Canada south to Texas and Virginia.

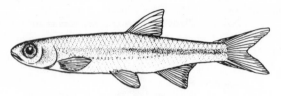

Figure 324

PLAINS SHINER, _Notropis percobromus_ (Cope).
 Resembles _N. atherinoides_ except eye is smaller and body is deeper. Teeth 2, 4-4, 2. Length 4 inches. Iowa to Texas.
 Notropis perpallidus Hubbs and Black.
 Individuals with front of dorsal fin far behind front of anal fin will key here. (See couplet 27a.)

RIO GRANDE SHINER, _Notropis jemezanus_ (Cope).............
..................................**(See Fig. 343, Couplet 44b.)**
 Slender or immature individuals may key here.

29b. Body dark above lateral line; base of anal fin more or less
pigmented **30**

30a. Less than 18 scales before dorsal fin; length of snout less than
diameter of eye. (See Fig. 321, couplet 27b.).................
.........**POPEYE SHINER, _Notropis ariommus telescopus_ (Cope)**
 Color as in _N. ariommus_. Upper Tennessee River drainage.

30b. More than 18 scales before dorsal fin; length of snout equal or
more than diameter of eye................................**31**

31a. Length of snout equal to diameter of eye. Fig. 325...........
..............**SILVERLINE SHINER _Notropis amoenus_ (Abbott)**
 Pale green back and silvery sides with faint lateral band. Teeth 2, 4-4, 2. Length 4 inches. New Jersey south to South Carolina.

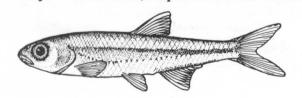

Figure 325

31b. Length of snout greater than diameter of eye. Fig. 326.......
.... ROSYFACE SHINER, *Notropis rubellus* (Agassiz)
Silvery with wide lateral band. Teeth 2, 4-4, 2. Length 4 inches.
North Dakota to the St. Lawrence and Hudson River and south to Virginia and part of the Ohio River drainage.

Figure 326

32a. Lateral line more or less incomplete (not reaching near base of caudal fin) 33

32b. Lateral line usually complete (extending nearly to base of caudal fin) 35

33a. Anal rays usually 7. (See Fig. 306, couplet 19a.) ....
.... BRIDLED SHINER, *Notropis bifrenatus* (Cope)
Usually a slender minnow, but heavy individuals will key here.

33b. Anal rays usually 8 or 9 34

34a. Lateral band extends through eye and touches chin; dark edges of scales in row above and in lateral line form a zigzag pattern. Fig. 327........ BLACKCHIN SHINER, *Notropis heterodon* (Cope)
Silvery. Lateral line extends only about ½ body length. Teeth vary from 4-4 to 1, 4-4, 1. Length 2½ inches. North Dakota to Quebec and south to New York and Iowa.

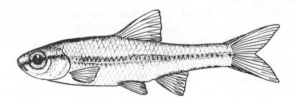

Figure 327

34b. Lateral band extends through eye and around snout, but does not touch chin; dark edges of scales in lateral line, form a band of crescent marks; lateral line variable, may extend much more than 1/2 body length. Fig. 328....................... BLACK-NOSE SHINER, *Notropis heterolepis* Eigenmann and Eigenmann

129

Silvery. Lateral line almost complete. Teeth 4-4. Length 2½ inches. Southern Canada to Maine and south to Iowa and the Ohio River drainage.

Figure 328

35a. **Mouth almost vertical and very small, extending only about halfway to the front of the eye. Fig. 329**........................
...................**PUGNOSE SHINER,** *Notropis anogenus* Forbes
Dark lateral band, chin black; faint caudal spot. Teeth 4-4. Length 2 inches. Eastern North Dakota to the St. Lawrence drainage, including northern Illinois, Indiana and Ohio.

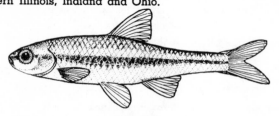

Figure 329

35b. **Mouth oblique to almost horizontal and extending to or almost to the front of the eye**......................................**36**
36a. **Anal rays usually 9 to 11**.....................................**37**
36b. **Anal rays usually 7 or 8**......................................**45**
37a. **Fins all heavily tipped with black pigment. (See Fig. 296, couplet 9a.)**...............**BLACKFIN SHINER,** *Notropis bellus* (Hay)
Young or slender individuals may key here.

37b. **Fins not all heavily tipped with black pigment** **38**

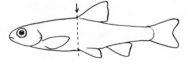

Figure 330

38a. **Front of dorsal fin above or slightly before or slightly behind front of pelvic fins. Fig. 330** **39**

38b. **Front of dorsal fin completely behind entire base of pelvic fins. Fig. 331**..............**41**

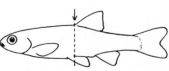

Figure 331

39a. Lateral band of pigment not developed on sides. (See Figs. 293-295, couplet 9a.)..COMMON SHINER, *Notropis cornutus* (Mitchill)

VIRGINIA SHINER, *Notropis cerasinus* (Cope).

WHITE SHINER, *Notropis albeolus* Jordan.
The adults are rather deep-bodied, but immature individuals may be more slender and key out here.

39b. Lateral band of pigment present on sides but may be faint or developed only on peduncle.................................**40**

40a. Lateral band of pigment more or less dusky but not black. SAFFRON SHINER, *Notropis rubricroceus* (Cope)............Fig. 332
Olivaceous with more or less red color; lateral band extends onto caudal fin; snout longer than eye diameter; maxillary reaches to or behind front of eye. Anal rays 8-9. Teeth 2, 4-4, 2. Length 4 inches. Headwaters of the Tennessee River.

Figure 332

SILVERSTRIPE SHINER, *Notropis illecebrosus* (Girard). Fig. 333.
Pale straw color with silvery band; snout shorter than diameter of eye; maxillary reaches to front of eye. Teeth 1, 4-4, 1. Length 3 inches. Iowa southward into Texas.

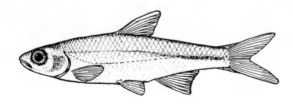

Figure 333

WHITETAIL SHINER, *Notropis galacturus* (Cope)........Fig. 334
Anal rays 8 or 9, individuals with 9 anal rays will key here. Females olivaceous, males steel blue above, white below. Caudal fin with distinct white area at base; dorsal fin with black blotch on posterior

131

rays. Teeth 1, 4-4, 1. Length 5-6 inches. Ozark streams in Missouri and Arkansas and headwaters of Cumberland and Tennessee Rivers.

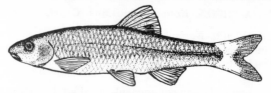

Figure 334

WARPAINT SHINER, *Notropis coccogenis* (Cope)........Fig..335
Anal rays 8-9, individuals with 9 anal rays will key here. Olivaceous above, silvery below, dark vertical bar just behind opercle. Spring males are rosy below and red on heads. Caudal fin with light basal area. Upper portion of dorsal fin black. Teeth 2, 4-4, 2. Length 5 inches. Headwaters of Cumberland and Tennessee Rivers.

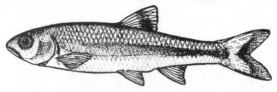

Figure 335

40b. Lateral band very dark (black) and well developed. BLEEDING SHINER, *Notropis zonatus* (Agassiz).....................Fig. 336
Olivaceous, no spots on fins; maxillary·does not quite reach front of eye. Males with bright red sides. Teeth 2, 4-4, 2. Length 5 inches. Ozark streams of Missouri and Arkansas.

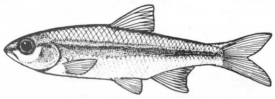

Figure 336

POPEYE SHINER, *Notropis ariommus* (Cope)...................
..................................(See **Fig. 321,** couplet 27b.)
Maxillary reaches front of eye. Usually slender, but stout individuals will key here.

Notropis trichroistius (Jordan and Gilbert)....................
..................................(See **Fig. 302,** couplet 13b.)
Rather deep bodied, but more slender individuals will key here.

41a. Scales in lateral line more than 40; scales before dorsal fin 29 to 30. Fig. 337.....REDFIN SHINER, *Notropis umbratilis* (Girard)

Rather deep-bodied, but immature individuals are more slender. (See Fig. 299, couplet 12a.)

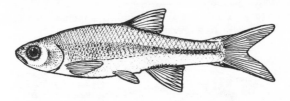

Figure 337

41b. Scales in lateral line less than 40; scales before dorsal fin less than 29...42

42a. Basal portion of caudal fin distinctly marked with white or light color.........SAILFIN SHINER, *Notropis hypselopterus* (Gunther)

Blotch in dorsal fin; 2 rosy spots at base of caudal fin. Usually a heavy-bodied fish, but more slender individuals will key here. (See Fig. 289, couplet 8a.)

Notropis xaenurus (Jordan).

Dark steel blue above; silvery below; caudal spot continuous with lateral band; upper posterior part of dorsal fin black. Teeth 1, 4-4, 1. Length 3 inches. Altamaha River drainage, Georgia.

42b. Basal portion of caudal fin not marked with white or light colored area 43

43a. Dorsal fin marked with a blotch. SNOWY SHINER, *Notropis niveus chloristius* (Jordan and Brayton)........................Fig. 338

Deep bodied forms of this species will key here. (See couplet 22b.)

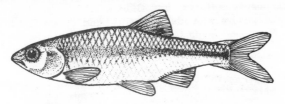

Figure 338

Notropis stonei Fowler...............(See Fig. 290, couplet 8a.)
Slender bodied individuals will key here.

43b. Dorsal fin without any blotch..............................**44**

44a. Scales before dorsal fin 20 or more. BLUNTNOSE SHINER, *Notropis simus* **(Cope)**...................................**Fig. 339**
Plain silvery. Teeth 1, 4-4, 1. Length 3½ inches. Rio Grande River drainage, Texas and New Mexico.

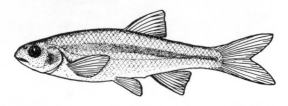

Figure 339

SHARPNOSE SHINER, *Notropis oxyrhynchus* **Hubbs and Bonham.**
....**Fig. 340**
Pale silvery sides with faint lateral band posteriorly. Teeth 2, 4-4, 2. Length 2½ inches. Brazos River, Texas.

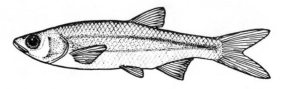

Figure 340

44b. Scales before dorsal fin less than 20. WATCHFUL SHINER, *Notropis scepticus* **(Jordan and Gilbert)**...................**Fig. 341**
Greenish silvery with silvery lateral band. Teeth 2, 4-4, 1. Length 3 inches. North and South Carolina to Florida.

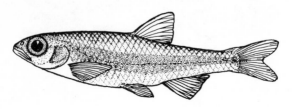

Figure 341

LOWLAND SHINER, *Notropis cummingsae* Myers........**Fig. 342**
Silvery with dark lateral band. Teeth 2, 4-4, 1. Length 3 inches. North and South Carolina.

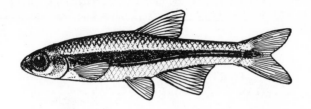

Figure 342

EMERALD SHINER, *Notropis atherinoides* Rafinesque...........
...................................(See Fig. 324, couplet 29a.)
Heavy bodied individuals will key here.

FLAGFIN SHINER, *Notropis signipinnis* Bailey and Suttkus......
...................................(See Fig. 291, couplet 8a.)
Silvery with very broad lateral band. Slender individuals will key here.

RIO GRANDE SHINER, *Notropis jemezanus* (Cope).......**Fig. 343**
Pale silvery with a lateral band best developed posteriorly. Lateral line well below lateral band. Teeth 2, 4-4, 2. Length 3 inches. Rio Grande River drainage and southward.

Figure 343

KANAWHA SHINER, *Notropis kanawha* Jordan and Jenkins.
More or less silvery; no pigment on fins or at base of caudal fin. Teeth 4-4. Length 3½ inches. Kanawha River drainage, West Virginia and Virginia.

45a. Lateral line scales 40 or more than 40.....................46

45b. Lateral line scales less than 40...........................48

46a. Basal portion of caudal fin not milky white. Fig. 344..........
................**SPOTTAIL SHINER,** *Notropis callistius* **(Jordan)**
Olivaceous; tip of dorsal fin white; caudal fin red but milky at tips; very large caudal spot. Similar to blacktail shiner, but has more scales in lateral line. Teeth 1, 4-4, 1. Length 4 inches. Alabama River drainage.

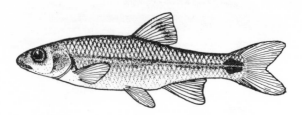

Figure 344

46b. Basal portion of caudal fin milky white......................**47**

47a. Snout slightly longer than diameter of eye; dark bar on sides just behind opercle. (See Fig. 335, couplet 40a)....................
................**WARPAINT SHINER,** *Notropis coccogenis* **(Cope)**
Anal rays 8-9; individuals with 8 anal rays will key here.

47b. Snout almost twice the diameter of the eye; no dark bar on sides back of opercle. (See Fig. 334, couplet 40a.)..................
................**WHITETAIL SHINER,** *Notropis galacturus* **(Cope)**
Anal rays 8-9; individuals with 8 anal rays will key here.

48a. No dark spot on or at the base of the caudal fin..............**49**

48b. A more or less distinct dark spot on or at the base of the caudal fin (may be fused with lateral band)........................**55**

49a. Upper lip considerably below level of lower margin of eye; mouth almost horizontal ....**LONG-**
SABINE SHINER, *Notropis sabinae* **Jordan and Gilbert. Fig. 345.**
Pale olive with very faint lateral band; maxillary extends past front of pupil; dorsal rays 8. Teeth 4-4. Length 2 inches. Southeastern Missouri into eastern Texas.

Figure 345

BLUNTNOSE SHINER, *Notropis simus* **(Cope)**..................
...................................**(See Fig. 339, couplet 44α.)**
Individuals with 8 anal rays will key here.

PROSPERINE SHINER, *Notropis prosperinus* **(Girard)....Fig. 346**
Silvery with lateral band on sides; maxillary extends almost to front
of orbit; anal rays 7. Teeth 4-4. Length 2 inches. Rio Grande River
drainage, Texas.

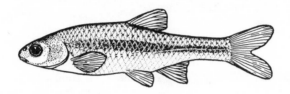

Figure 346

49b. Upper lip on or above level with lower margin of eye; mouth
more or less oblique...**50**

50α. Maxillary extending past front of eye; lateral band very dark.
BIGEYE SHINER, *Notropis boops* Gilbert...............**Fig. 347**
Olivaceous with dusky sides; lateral band passes through eye
and over snout. Teeth 1, 4-4, 1. Length 3 inches. Most of Ohio River
drainage and southwest into Oklahoma.

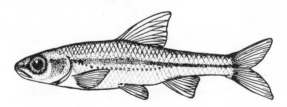

Figure 347

SAFFRON SHINER, *Notropis rubricroceus* **(Cope)**..............
...................................**(See Fig. 332, couplet 40α.)**
Individuals with 8 anal rays will key here.

50b. Maxillary not extending back of front margin of eye.........51

51a. Lateral band dark and may be narrow. **ROUGH HEAD SHINER,** *Notropis scabriceps* (Cope).............................**Fig. 348**
Olivaceous with dusky lateral band which extends forward onto snout. Teeth 2, 4-4, 2. Length 3 inches. Upper drainage of the Kanawha River, Virginia and West Virginia.

Figure 348

KIAMICHI SHINER, *Notropis ortenburgeri* Hubbs...............
....................................(See Fig. 320, couplet 27a.)
Deep bodied individuals will key here.

BLACKNOSE SHINER, *Notropis heterolepis* Eigenmann and Eigenmann..............................(See Fig. 328, couplet 34b.)
Lateral line variable; individuals with complete lateral line will key here.

51b. Lateral band rather pale...................................**52**

52a. Snout shorter than diameter of eye. Fig. 349.................
....................**SAND SHINER,** *Notropis stramineus* (Cope)
Silvery. Teeth 4-4. Length 2½ inches. Several subspecies, North Dakota to the St. Lawrence and Ohio River drainages and south to Mexico.

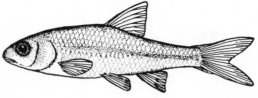

Figure 349

52b. Snout equal to or longer than diameter of eye...............**53**

53a. No pigment on scales at base of anal fin. Fig. 350...........
....................**RIVER SHINER,** *Notropis blennius* (Girard)
Pale olive. Teeth variable, (1)2, 4-4, 1(2) or 4-4. Length 2½ inches. Eastern Wyoming and Alberta to Pennsylvania and south to Tennessee and Texas.

Figure 350

53b. Pigment present on scales at base of anal fin.................54

54a. Scales before dorsal fin more than 16. Fig. 351...............
................BIGMOUTH SHINER, *Notropis dorsalis* (Agassiz)
Olivaceous above and silvery below. Region in front of dorsal fin
more or less scaleless. Teeth 1, 4-4, 1. Length 3½ inches. North Dakota
and Missouri eastward through the Great Lakes drainage to New York.

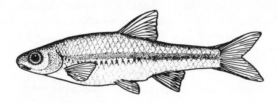

Figure 351

54b. Scales before dorsal fin less than 16..........................
...................MIMIC SHINER, *Notropis volucellus* (Cope)
Heavier bodied individuals will key here. (See Fig. 307, couplet
20a.)

GHOST SHINER, *Notropis buchanani* Meek.............Fig. 352
Very similar to *N. volucellus* but more pale and with higher lateral
line scales. Teeth 4-4. Length 2½ inches. Minnesota through the Ohio
River drainage and south to Texas.

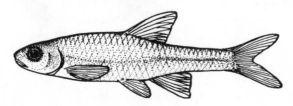

Figure 352

PALLID SHINER, *Notropis amnis* **Hubbs and Greene....Fig. 353**
Silvery. Teeth 1, 4-4, 1. Length 2½ inches. Several subspecies. Southern Minnesota and Indiana to eastern Texas.

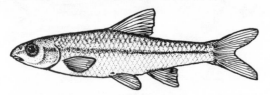

Figure 353

55a. Anal rays usually 7 (except in the blacktail shiner with a larger black caudal spot, which has 7 to 8 anal rays)................56

55b. Anal rays usually 8.......................................62

56a. Sides above lateral line with large (large as eye) irregular spots. Fig. 354.....CHIHUAHUA SHINER, *Notropis chihuahua* **Woolman**
Light brown with spots. Teeth 4-4. Length 2 inches. Mexico north into the Rio Grande drainage of Texas.

Figure 354

56b. Sides above lateral line not marked with large spots.........57

57a. Caudal spot larger than eye. Fig. 355.......................
................BLACKTAIL SHINER, *Notropis venustus* **(Girard)**
Rather deep bodied, but slender individuals with only 7 anal rays will key here. (See couplet 5a.)

Figure 355

57b. Caudal spot smaller than eye..............................58

58a. Snout shorter than diameter of eye. Fig. 356..................
..........BLACKSPOT SHINER, *Notropis atrocaudalis* Evermann
Olivaceous; lateral band extending through eye and snout. Teeth
4-4. Length 2½ inches. Oklahoma and Texas.

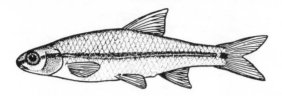

Figure 356

Notropis xaenocephalus (Jordan)......(See Fig. 310, couplet 20b.)
Deeper bodied individuals will key here. Resembles the weed shiner but has 13 scales before the dorsal fin instead of 15 and has more
decurved lateral line.

CENTRAL WEED SHINER, *Notropis texanus* (Girard)............
..................................(See Fig. 359, couplet 60a.)
Individuals with short snouts will key here.

58b. Snout equal to or longer than diameter of eye................59

59a. Lateral band does not pass through eye and over snout..WEST-
ERN LONGNOSE SHINER, *Notropis bairdi* Hubbs and Ortenburger
....Fig. 357
Silvery, somewhat dusky above; caudal spot mostly on caudal rays;
black spot at base of center of dorsal fin. Teeth 4-4. Length 2 inches.
Oklahoma and Texas.

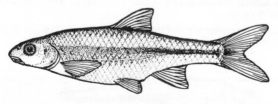

Figure 357

Notropis asperifrons Suttkus and Bailey.(See Fig. 314, couplet 21a.)
Deeper bodied individuals will key here.

BROADHEAD SHINER, *Notropis potteri* Hubbs and Bonham....
....**Fig. 358**
Dusky above, silvery below. Similar to western longnose shiner.
Teeth 2, 4-4, 2. Length 2½ inches. Brazos River system and perhaps
Red River, Texas.

Figure 358

Notropis hypsilepis **Suttkus and Raney.**
Deeper bodied individuals will key here. See couplet 20b.

59b. Lateral line passes through eye and on snout................**60**

60a. Lateral band touches chin. **Fig. 359**........................
.............**CENTRAL WEED SHINER, *Notropis texanus* (Girard)**
Olivaceous above, silvery below. Teeth 2, 4-4, 2. Length 2½ inches.
Georgia and western Florida to Texas.

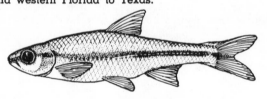

Figure 359

Subspecies *N. r. richardsonius* extends northward into Minnesota
and Michigan. (See Fig. 312, couplet 20b.)

60b. Lateral band confined to snout and does not touch chin......**61**

61a. Snout longer than diameter of eye and rather pointed, protruding slightly beyond upper lip. **COASTAL SHINER, *Notropis petersoni* Fowler**...**Fig. 360**
Dusky above, silvery below. Teeth 2, 4-4, 2. Length 2 inches. North
Carolina into Alabama and northern Florida.

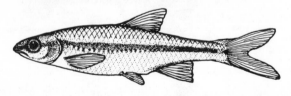

Figure 360

Notropis baileyi Suttkus and Raney.....................Fig. 361

Dusky above and silvery below with a lateral band from snout to prominent spot at base of caudal fin. Teeth 2, 4-4, 2. Length 2½ inches. Alabama River, Tombigbee River, and Pascagoula River drainages of Mississippi and Alabama.

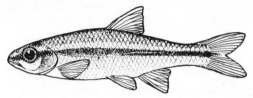

Figure 361

BLACKSPOT SHINER, *Notropis atrocaudalis* Evermann..........
...................................(See Fig. 356, couplet 58a.)
Individuals with a longer snout will key here.

61b. **Snout short, not longer than diameter of eye and rather rounded, not extending beyond upper lip.** *Notropis alborus* **Hubbs and Raney**..Fig. 362

Dusky above and silvery below. Teeth 4-4. Length 2 inches. Roanoke River in Virginia to Santee River in South Carolina.

Figure 362

SWALLOWTAIL SHINER, *Notropis procne* (Cope)..............
...................................(See Fig. 308, couplet 20a.)
Rather heavy bodied individuals will key here. Snout is short but rather sharp instead of rounded.

TOPEKA SHINER, *Notropis topeka* Gilbert....................
...................................(See Fig. 287, couplet 7b.)
Eye smaller than in *N. alborus*. Slender individuals will key here.

COLORED SHINER, *Notropis chrosomus* (Jordan)..............
...................................(See Fig. 364, couplet 64a.)
Individuals with 7 anal rays will key here.

62a. Mouth very oblique and small, extending only about 2/3 the length of the snout. Fig. 363.....................................
.............IRONCOLOR SHINER, *Notropis chalybaeus* (Cope)

Dark above and silvery below with a very black lateral band which extends through eye and snout. Small detached black spot at base of caudal fin. Teeth 2, 4-4, 2. Length 2 inches. Coastal lowlands, New Jersey to Texas and north in Mississippi drainage to Iowa.

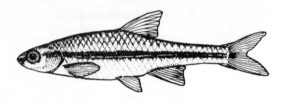

Figure 363

62b. Mouth moderate length, reaching to or almost to front of eye..**63**

63a. Spot at base of caudal fin very dark.......................**64**

63b. Spot at base of caudal fin rather pale, not large............**66**

64a. Caudal spot not detached from lateral band. **COLORED SHINER**, *Notropis chrosomus* (Jordan)........................**Fig. 364**

Dusky above, silvery below. Males with scarlet band above lateral band and scarlet bar across anal, dorsal and caudal fins. Teeth 2, 4-4, 2. Length 3 inches. Alabama River drainage.

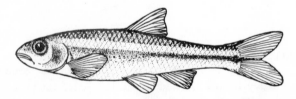

Figure 364

Notropis xaenocephalus (Jordan.)

Individuals with 8 anal rays will key here. (See Fig. 310, couplet 20b.)

64b. Caudal spot detached from lateral band....................**65**

65a. Caudal spot triangular; scales at base of anal fin well pigmented. Fig. 365...

WEDGESPOT SHINER, *Notropis greenei* (Hubbs and Ortenburger)

Dusky above, pale below. Length 2½ inches. Ozark drainage of Arkansas and eastern Oklahoma.

Figure 365

65b. Caudal spot not triangular but more or less rounded; scales at base of anal fin not pigmented. Fig. 366.......................

..................SPOTTAIL SHINER, *Notropis hudsonius* (Clinton)

Pale silvery with more or less dusky lateral band. Teeth 4-4. Length 4-6 inches. North Dakota and adjacent Manitoba to the Hudson River and south to Virginia, Illinois and Iowa.

Figure 366

66a. Front of dorsal fin distinctly before front of pelvic fins. Fig. 367..

....ARKAN-

SAS RIVER SHINER, *Notropis girardi* Hubbs and Ortenburger

Dusky above, pale below; mouth subterminal and rather horizontal. Length 2 inches. Arkansas River drainage, Arkansas and Oklahoma.

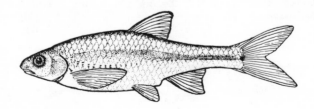

Figure 367

66b. Front of dorsal fin over or behind front of pelvic fins. TEXAS SHINER, *Notropis amabilis* **(Girard)**....................Fig. 368

Olivaceous above, silvery below; front of dorsal fin above or slightly behind front of pelvic fins. Teeth 2, 4-4, 2. Length 2½ inches. Texas southward into Mexico.

Figure 368

BRAZOS RIVER SHINER, *Notropis brazosensis* **Hubbs and Bonham**...Fig. 369

Pale silvery with some pigment above lateral line; silvery lateral band with a dark streak above on sides; front of dorsal fin above or slightly behind front of pelvic fins. Teeth 1, 4-4, 1. Length 2½ inches. Eastern Texas.

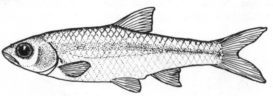

Figure 369

YELLOWFIN SHINER, *Notropis lutipinnis* **(Jordan and Brayton).**
....Fig. 370

Dusky green above, silvery below; dorsal fin entirely behind pelvic fins. Teeth 2, 4-4, 2. Length 2½ inches. Santee River drainage, North and South Carolina.

Notropis callisema **(Jordan).**

Bluish above, silvery below; large dark spot on last rays of dorsal fin; white tips on dorsal, anal, and caudal fins; dark lateral band ending in caudal spot. Teeth 4-4. Length 2¾ inches. Altamaha River drainage, Georgia.

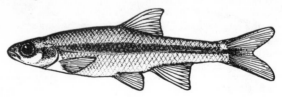

Figure 370

BLUESTRIPE SHINER, Notropis callitaenia Bailey and Gibbs.
Very similar to N. callisema. Teeth 1, 4-4, 1. Apalachicola River and Escambia River drainages, Georgia, Alabama, and Florida.
Notropis caeruleus (Jordan).
Bluish above, silvery white below; lateral band continuous with inconspicuous caudal spot; faint blotch in upper posterior part of dorsal fin; milky white tips on dorsal, anal, and caudal fins. Teeth 1, 4-4, 1. Length 3 inches. Alabama River basin.
Notropis leedsi Fowler.
Slender individuals will key here. (See couplet 7b.)

BLACKTAIL SHINER, Notropis venustus (Girard)...............
............(See Fig. 284, couplet 5a and Fig. 355, couplet 57a.)
Slender forms with faint caudal spots will key here.

CATFISH FAMILY, Ictaluridae (Ameiuridae)

The members of this family are readily distinguished by their scaleless bodies, broad flat heads, sharp heavy pectoral and dorsal spines, and long barbels about the mouth. They possess bands of numerous bristle-like teeth in the upper jaw. Their barbels are arranged in a definite pattern, four under the jaws, two above and one on each tip of the maxillary. Originally the family Ictaluridae was found in the United States only east of the Rockies, but now various species have been widely introduced in the western states. All the larger species are desirable food fishes. This family includes the large catfishes, the bullheads, and the small madtoms. The latter are noted for venomous glands in their spines. All catfishes possess glands which cause a prick from their spines to be quite irritating, but the small madtoms have glands which seem to be more virulent.

These fishes are all more or less omnivorous, feeding on all manner of animal food and often on vegetable matter. They are mostly nocturnal and use their barbels to locate their food. They are nesting fishes, spawning in the spring or early summer and depositing their eggs in some sort of a depression or cavity. The male assumes care of the eggs and guards the young for several weeks after hatching.

The marine catfishes belong to another family and can be recognized by having fewer barbels. The GAFFTOPSAIL CATFISH, Bagre marinus (Mitchill) and the SEA CATFISH, Galeichthys felis (Linnaeus), found in the seas from Cape Cod to Texas, may occasionally enter freshwater. These are bluish silver catfishes with deeply forked tails. The gafftopsail catfish has 4 barbels on the head, and the sea catfish has 6 barbels on the head.

1a. Caudal fin deeply forked....................................2

1b. Caudal fin not deeply forked, but rounded or square..........4

2a. Anal fin with 30 or more rays. Fig. 371.....................
.....................**BLUE CATFISH,** *Ictalurus furcatus* **(LeSueur)**
Silvery white below shading to dusky blue on back. Reaches weight of over 50 pounds. Large rivers from Minnesota and Ohio southward into Mexico.

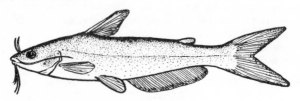

Figure 371

2b. Anal fin with less than 30 rays...............................**3**

3a. Anal fin with 19 to 23 rays. Fig. 372...........................
.....................**WHITE CATFISH,** *Ictalurus catus* **(Linnaeus)**
Bluish above and silvery below. Reaches a length of 2 feet. Coastal streams from Chesapeake Bay region and southward to Texas; widely introduced on west coast.

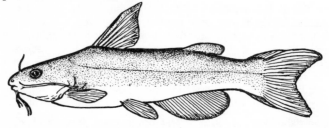

Figure 372

3b. Anal fin with 24-29 rays. Fig. 373............................
...........**CHANNEL CATFISH,** *Ictalurus punctatus* **(Rafinesque)**
Whitish below and on sides, bluish on back, sides with small irregular spots. Reaches a weight of over 20 pounds. Great Lakes and Sashatchewan River southward to Gulf and Mexico.

Figure 373

4a. Adipose fin free, not fused to caudal fin 5

4b. Adipose fin not free but fused to caudal fin or separated by a slight or incomplete notch 9

5a. Anal rays less than 16; band of teeth in upper jaw with backward lateral extensions (Fig. 374). Fig. 375 . . . .
. . . . .FLATHEAD CATFISH, *Pylodictis olivaris* (Rafinesque)

Yellowish brown above, pale gray below and often mottled on sides. Reaches a weight of over 100 pounds. Large rivers, Mississippi valley into Mexico.

Figure 374

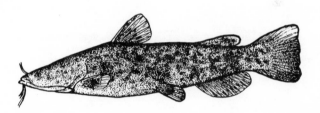

Figure 375

5b. Anal fin with more than 16 rays; band of teeth in upper jaw without any backward lateral extensions (Fig. 376). (Formerly *Ameiurus*, BULLHEADS, but now part of *Ictalurus*) 6

Figure 376

6a. Barbels under jaw whitish; anal rays 23 to 27 . . . .
. . . . .YELLOW BULLHEAD, *Ictalurus natalis* (LeSueur)
Color variable, back various shades of brown to almost black; belly more or less yellow. Reaches a length of 18 inches. North Dakota to the Hudson River and southward.

6b. Barbels under jaw dark; anal rays less than 24..................7

7a. Pectoral spine strongly barbed on posterior edge (Fig. 377), offers
resistance when grasped by thumb and forefinger. Fig. 378......
..............BROWN BULLHEAD, *Ictalurus nebulosus* (LeSueur)

Back more or less dark brown, belly gray to yellowish; sides and back often mottled. Reaches a
length of 18 inches. Maine and Great Lakes to Florida
and Mexico. Introduced elsewhere.

Figure 377

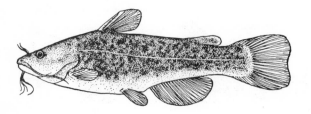

Figure 378

7b. Pectoral spine weakly barbed on posterior edge
(Fig. 379), offers little resistance when grasped by
thumb and forefinger...........................8

Figure 379

8a. Head broad and flat; body elongated; 16-20 anal rays.........
...............FLAT BULLHEAD, *Ictalurus platycephalus* (Girard)
Various shades of olive brown to yellowish brown. Reaches a
length of 15 inches. Coastal streams, North Carolina to northern Florida.

8b. Head not so broad and flat; body shorter; 17-24 anal rays. Fig. 380..............BLACK BULLHEAD, *Ictalurus melas* (Rafinesque)
Dark above, ranging from yellowish brown to almost black. Belly varies from yellow to gray. Reaches a length of 18 inches. New York and North Dakota to Texas. Introduced elsewhere.

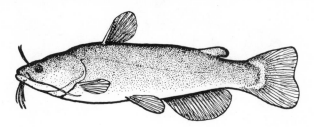

Figure 380

9a. Teeth in upper jaw (See Fig. 374) are in bands with backward lateral extensions. Fig. 381.....................................
.......................STONECAT, *Noturus flavus* (Rafinesque)
Color yellowish brown to gray. Reaches length of 12 inches. Montana to Great Lakes and south to Texas.

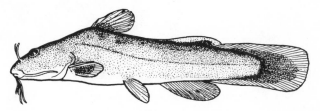

Figure 381

9b. Teeth of upper jaw are in bands without backward lateral extensions (See Fig. 376), MADTOMS, (formerly *Schilbeodes*).....10

10a. Pectoral spine not barbed on posterior margin (spine must be dissected loose from membrane)............................11

10b. Pectoral spine more or less strongly barbed on posterior surface (several species have only several barbs near the base of spine) 12

11a. Color more or less plain. Fig. 382......*Noturus gyrinus* (Mitchill)
Yellowish brown to gray above, pale below. Reaches length of five inches. North Dakota to Quebec and south to Florida and Texas. Introduced into Columbia River drainage.

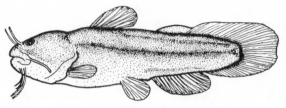

Figure 382

11b. Slightly mottled. Fig. 383........ *Noturus leptacanthus* Jordan
Yellowish brown and somewhat mottled. Reaches length of 3 inches. Pectoral spine barbed on anterior margin. South Carolina to Louisiana.

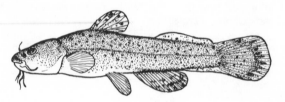

Figure 383

12a. Adipose fin not separated from caudal fin by a distinct notch..13

12b. Adipose fin separated from caudal fin by a more or less distinct notch 14

13a. Anal fin with 15-16 anal rays, few barbs on pectoral spine near base. Fig. 384............*Noturus nocturnus* Jordan and Gilbert
Dark brown speckled with black. Reaches a length of about 3 inches. Indiana to Oklahoma.

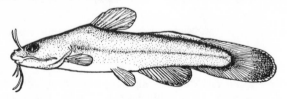

Figure 384

13b. Anal fin with more than 18 rays; color dark. Fig. 385..........
..............................*Noturus funebris* Jordan and Swain
Rather blackish; fins with dusky margins. Reaches length of
about 4 inches. Florida to Louisiana.

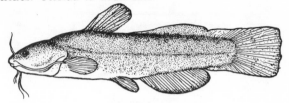

Figure 385

**14a. Length of barbs of pectoral spine not exceeding 1/2 diameter of
pectoral spine** **15**

**14b. Length of barbs of pectoral spine more than 1/2 diameter of
pectoral spine** **18**

**15a. Notch does not completely separate adipose fin from caudal
fin** **16**

15b. Notch completely separates adipose fin from caudal fin......**17**

16a. Pectoral spine is very short, about 3 times in head. Fig. 386....
....*Noturus exilis* Nelson
Dark brown, faint blotch about base of dorsal fin. Reaches length
of over six inches. Southern Minnesota to West Virginia, south into
Oklahoma.

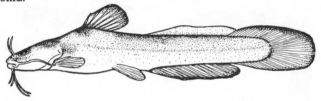

Figure 386

**16b. Pectoral spine is moderate length, about 2 times in head length.
Fig. 387**...........................*Noturus insignis* (Richardson)
Dusky color; fins tend to have blackish margins. Length 5-6 inches.
Mostly east of Appalachians. New York to Georgia.

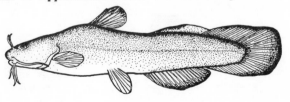

Figure 387

153

17a. Lower lobe of caudal black; barbs on pectoral spine only at the base. Fig. 388........*Noturus gilberti* Jordan and Evermann Dark yellowish brown. Length 4 inches. Roanoke River, Virginia.

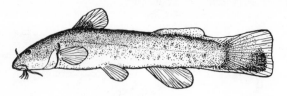

Figure 388

17b. Caudal with dusky bar on base and diffuse sub-marginal band; body with 4 inconspicuous saddle-like blotches...............
......................*Noturus hildebrandi* (Bailey and Taylor) Dusky color. Southwestern Mississippi.

18a. Caudal fin dark except for whitish rim; bar across tip of dorsal and anal fins. Color nearly plain with faint saddle-like blotches. Fig. 389............................*Noturus eleutherus* Jordan Rather brown in color. Length 4 inches. Michigan and Ohio to western North Carolina and eastern Oklahoma and Kansas.

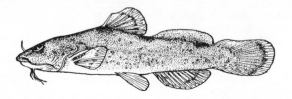

Figure 389

18b. Color mottled with dark saddle-like blotches................19

19a. Anterior edge of pectoral spine with few barbs. Fig. 390.......
....*Noturus miurus* Jordan Grayish color with dorsal blotches. Length about 4 inches. Illinois to southern Ontario and to Mississippi and Oklahoma.

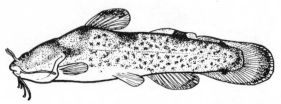

Figure 390

19b. **Anterior edge of pectoral spine with many barbs. Fig. 391......**
.............................*Noturus furiosus* **Jordan and Meek**
Brown speckled with black and dark dorsal blotches. Length about 5 inches. Eastern North Carolina.

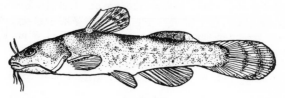

Figure 391

Several species of subterranean catfishes, the WIDEMOUTH BLINDCAT, *Satan eurystomus* Hubbs and Bailey and the TOOTHLESS BLINDCAT, *Trogoglanis pattersoni* Eigenmann are known from artesian wells in Texas. These are blind and without any pigment in their skin.

FRESHWATER EEL FAMILY, Anguillidae

The freshwater eel family is represented in the United States by one species, the AMERICAN EEL, *Anguilla rostrata* (LeSueur), (Fig. 392). This fish occurs in brackish waters along both the Atlantic and Gulf coasts and enters the rivers often penetrating to the headwaters.

The body is very long and slender, reaching a length of over two feet. The skin is yellowish brown and has a smooth appearance

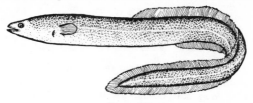

Figure 392

as the scales are minute and imbedded. The dorsal fin is very long and is continuous with the caudal and the anal fins. The pelvic fins are absent. The opercular margin is partly fused to the body, leaving only a small gill aperture.

The eel is a catadromous fish, living in freshwater but spawning in the deep Atlantic near Bermuda. The adults apparently die after spawning as they are seen no more. The eels have a very high reproductive potential, females often containing over 10,000,000 eggs. The tiny larval eels after hatching do not look like eels and are called *leptocephala*. They make their way to the mouths of the rivers where they grow into tiny eels four to six inches long. The males remain in the lower part of the river and never become very large. The females make their way upstream to the headwater pools and quiet stretches, traveling mostly at night. The eels remain in freshwater until they are sexually mature, the females reaching a length of 3 to 4 feet in five to seven years. When sexually mature, the females migrate downstream joining the males and swimming out into the ocean.

Eels occur in most of the rivers of the Atlantic and Gulf drainages. Eels are omnivorous, feeding on all kinds of animal food, both dead and alive. They are nocturnal in habits and have the ability to wriggle about on land for several hours. Eels are important for food in many places and are sometimes caught and sold commercially.

NEEDLEFISH FAMILY, Belonidae

This is a family of very slender marine fishes with both jaws elongated like a beak and bearing a superficial resemblance to the gars. The ATLANTIC NEEDLEFISH, *Strongylura marina* (Walbaum) (Fig. 393) enters freshwater and ascends rivers from Cape Cod to Texas. This is a greenish silvery fish with a narrow lateral band, reaching a length of four feet although most specimens caught are much smaller.

Figure 393

COD FAMILY, Gadidae

The Cod family is an important marine family with several species entering or living in freshwater. The members of this family are characterized by a long soft dorsal fin which in some species may be divided into 2 or 3 parts. They bear a single barbel under the chin and possess small pelvic fins which are located under the throat (jugular).

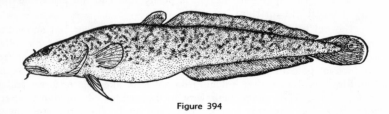

Figure 394

The FRESHWATER BURBOT, *Lota lota* (Linnaeus), (Fig. 394), is the only strictly freshwater species of cod found in North America. It is grayish olive and highly mottled with very minute scales. It reaches a length of 30 inches and a weight of over 10 pounds. The burbot is commonly found in larger lakes and often in very deep water. It spawns in the middle of winter either in shallow water or in streams. It ranges through the Great Lakes region and extreme northern Mississippi drainage of Wisconsin and Minnesota, and the upper Missouri River drainage, northwestward into Alaska and Siberia.

The TOMCOD, *Microgadus tomcod* (Walbaum) (Fig. 395) is a marine cod which commonly enters freshwater near the sea to spawn. This is a mottled olive brown fish with the dorsal fin divided into three parts. It reaches a length of 12 inches. The tomcod ranges from Laborador to Virginia.

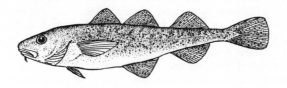

Figure 395

STICKLEBACK FAMILY, Gasterosteidae

The sticklebacks are all small fishes with slender stream-lined bodies. They are characterized by a series of free dorsal spines in front of the soft dorsal fin. The pelvic fins are reduced to heavy spines. Several species occur in the sea and may enter freshwater. Only one species is restricted to freshwater, the other species living equally well in fresh or salt water.

Sticklebacks lack scales. The marine forms tend to have heavy bony plates on their sides, but the freshwater forms, even the marine forms living in freshwater, have the body naked.

The sticklebacks build elaborate nests. The males construct the nest about the size of a golf ball penetrated by a tunnel used for the eggs. The nest is composed of grasses or fibers cemented together by a secretion of the male. The male cares for the eggs and watches after the newly hatched young.

Sticklebacks are noted for their pugnacious habits attacking fishes many times their size who intrude near their nests. They are predaceous feeding on small or minute aquatic animals.

157

1a. Gill membranes joined to each other forming a fold across the isthmus. Fig. 396.2

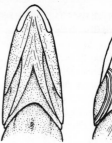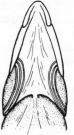

1b. Gill membranes not joined together but joined separately to the isthmus. Fig. 397....3

Figure 396   Figure 397

2a. Free dorsal spines usually 9 (8-11). Fig. 398...................
    ....NINESPINE STICKLEBACK, *Pungitius pungitius* (Linnaeus)
    Body very slender with long caudal peduncle. Brownish green above, silvery below and irregularly barred. Length 3 inches. Fresh and brackish waters of Northern Hemisphere. In the U. S. it is found in the Hudson Bay drainage of Minnesota, the Great Lakes, and as far south as New Jersey on the Atlantic coast.

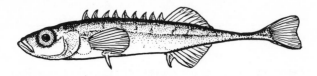

Figure 398

2b. Free dorsal spines usually 5 (4-6). Fig. 399...................
    ....BROOK STICKLEBACK, *Eucalia inconstans* (Kirtland)
    Body stout but rather streamlined. Brown to black above and light below; mottled on sides and finely speckled below. Length 2½ inches. Western Canada, Montana to Maine and south to Kansas, Illinois, Indiana, and Ohio.

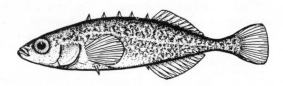

Figure 399

3a. Free dorsal spines usually 3. Fig. 400.........................
.....THREESPINE STICKLEBACK, *Gasterosteus aculeatus* Linnaeus

Body rather stout; brownish green above and light below, profusely speckled with black. Sides may be covered by bony plates or may be naked. Length 4 inches. Freshwater and marine in Northern Hemisphere. In the U. S. it occurs along the Pacific and Atlantic coasts and in the coastal streams.

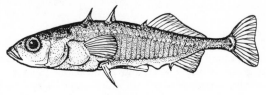

Figure 400

3b. Free dorsal spines usually 4. Fig. 401.........................
.........FOURSPINE STICKLEBACK, *Apeltes quadracus* (Mitchill)

Body streamlined with very slender caudal peduncle. Brownish green to black above, silvery below and rather mottled. Length 2½ inches. Marine, Atlantic coast from Virginia northward, sometimes entering coastal streams.

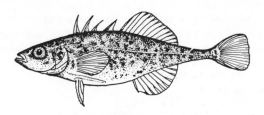

Figure 401

PIPEFISH FAMILY, Syngnathidae

This family contains the pipefishes and sea horses which are found in the warmer seas of the world. Although marine, pipefishes sometimes enter the mouths of rivers and in the southern United States the southern PIPEFISH, *Syngnathus scovelli* (Evermann and Kendall) (Fig. 402) may be found some distance inland. Pipefishes are very long and slender with prehensile tails by which they cling to vegetation. They

Figure 402

appear to be jointed as their bodies are covered by ring-like plates. Their snout is exceedingly long and bears small jaws at the tip. The males have abdominal pouches in which they carry the eggs placed there by the females. They reach a length of about 5 inches.

CAVEFISH FAMILY, Amblyopsidae

Although the members of this family are known as cave or blind fishes, several have functional eyes and may be found in springs and swamps. They are usually pale and rather colorless fishes which appear to be naked as their scales are minute and imbedded. They have flat naked heads and have many papilose sensory structures on their heads and bodies. Their eyes are degenerate or are poorly developed. The pelvic fins are either absent or are small. In the adults the anus moves anteriorly and is located in the throat (jugular). The females retain the fertilized eggs and give birth to living young.

Members of this family are usually found in underground streams of the limestone regions of Kentucky, Missouri, Arkansas, southern Illinois, southern Indiana and Tennessee. One species occurs in the swamps of the southeastern United States.

1a. Pelvic fins absent...2
1b. Pelvic fins present. Fig. 403....................................
.....MAMMOUTH CAVE BLINDFISH, *Amblyopsis spelaea* DeKay

Pale and rather colorless. Length 5 inches. In subterranean streams of the cave regions of Kentucky and southern Indiana. A closely related species, *Amblyopsis rosae* (Eigenmann), is found in caves of southeastern Missouri and Arkansas.

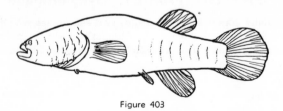

Figure 403

2a. Eyes rudimentary and concealed; body colorless, without pigment
............SMALL BLINDFISH, Typhlichthys subterraneus Girard
Length 2 inches. Streams in cave regions of Kentucky, Tennessee,
Alabama and Missouri.

Typhlichthys wyandotte Eigenmann in cave streams of southern
Indiana is similar, if not the same species.

2b. Eyes developed and not concealed; body dark, pigment present
in skin 3

3a. Body with ridges of papillae; caudal fin dark brown with several
vertical rows of white specks or blotches. Fig. 404.............
.................SPRING CAVEFISH, Chologaster agassizi Putnam
Brown above, lighter below, entire body sprinkled with black specks.
Three dark longitudinal stripes on sides. Center stripe may become
pale. Length 1½ inches. Springs in southern Illinois, Kentucky and
Tennessee.

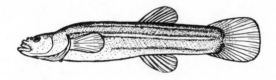

Figure 404

3b. Body without ridges or papillae; caudal fin with black blotch at
base, behind which is a white blotch or 2 white spots (may form
a bar); remainder of fin is black................................
..............SWAMP BLINDFISH, Chologaster cornutus Agassiz
Dark brown above, whitish below, entire body sprinkled with black
specks. Three black longitudinal stripes on sides. Dorsal fin white,
may be edged with black. Length up to 2 inches. Found in lowland
swamps from southern Virginia to Florida.

KILLIFISH FAMILY, Cyprinodontidae

The killifishes and topminnows are small fishes found in fresh
and salt water. Some are deep-bodied, and others are quite slender.
Many species show strong differences in the color and markings of
the sexes.

They possess more or less protruding lower jaws and tilted mouths
which are well adjusted for surface feeding. Their lateral line is incomplete or only partially developed.

Many species live in the sea, and some of these may enter freshwater. A number of other species are restricted to freshwater. Several

species are isolated in springs of the deserts of the southwestern United States and have become highly modified, some losing or reducing their pelvic fins. Killifishes feed on small crustacea and other small aquatic animals. They spawn in the spring or early summer.

1a. Teeth incisor-like and notched, with 2 or 3 cusps. Fig. 405.............................2

1b. Teeth pointed or conical, not with several cusps 5

Figure 405

2a. Teeth with 2 cusps................................*Crenichthys*
Olivaceous fishes restricted to several desert streams.

RAILROAD VALLEY SPRINGFISH, *Crenichthys nevadae* Hubbs. Fig. 406. Single row of spots on sides. Railroad Valley, Nevada.

WHITE RIVER SPRINGFISH, *Crenichthys baileyi* (Gilbert). Double row of spots on sides. Moapa River, California, and in White River and Pahranagat valleys, Nevada.

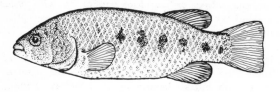

Figure 406

2b. Teeth with 3 cusps..3

3a. Dorsal fin long, 16-18 rays; first ray a stout grooved spine......
....*Jordanella*
FLAGFISH, *Jordanella floridae* Goode and Bean. Fig. 407. A deep-bodied fish, olivaceous with orange or brassy sides and 4-5 diffuse dark cross bars. Gill membrane joined to shoulder a short distance above base of pectoral fin. Each series of scales form a broad longitudinal stripe; large diffuse spot on side below front of dorsal fin. Fins dusky, may be speckled or barred, and may have a spot in posterior part of

dorsal fin. Length 2½ inches. Coastal swamps and lagoons from Florida to Yucatan.

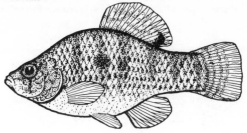

Figure 407

3b. Dorsal fin short, 10-12 rays; first dorsal ray not spine-like, but usually slender and rudimentary..............................4

4a. Opercular opening closed above by union of gill membrane to shoulder just above base of pectoral fin..............*Cyprinodon* VARIEGATED CYPRINODON, *Cyprinodon variegatus* Lacépède. Fig. 408. Deep bodied; very large humeral scale; dorsal rays 11; anal rays 10. Olivaceous; males deeply lustrous with salmon color belly; dorsal fin blackish with orange margin; caudal fin olive with black margin; anal and pelvic fins dusky with orange margins. Females lighter and with numerous cross bars. Young have black spots in dorsal fin near posterior tip. Length 2-3 inches. Widespread in fresh and brackish water along the coast from Cape Cod to the Rio Grande River.

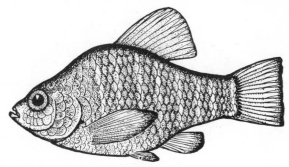

Figure 408

LAKE EUSTIS CYPRINODON, *Cyprinodon hubbsi* Carr. Closely related, but is restricted to Florida.

RED RIVER CYPRINODON, *Cyprinodon rubrofluviatilis* Fowler. Fig. 409. Rather slender; body depth about three times in length; dorsal rays 9; anal rays 8-9. Length 1½ inches. Texas and southern Oklahoma.

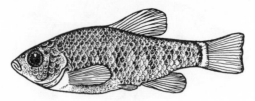

Figure 409

LEON SPRING CYPRINODON, *Cyprinodon bovinus* Baird and Girard found formerly at Leon Springs in southeastern Texas was very similar.

TEXAS CYPRINODON, *Cyprinodon elegans* Baird and Girard is another closely related form from the Comanche Springs and Phantom Lake, Texas. Extinct.

DESERT CYPRINODON, *Cyprinodon macularius* Baird and Girard. Fig. 410. Variable in color, usually dusky with light underparts; fins usually margined with black. Females with dark cross bars on sides. Dorsal fin may have a blotch posteriorly. Humeral scale not much enlarged; dorsal rays 9-11; anal rays 10-11. Desert streams of southern Nevada and Utah and southeastern California. Many related species in desert water holes as follows:

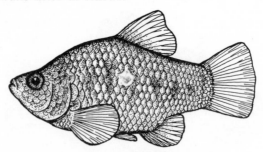

Figure 410

NEVADA CYPRINODON, *Cyprinodon nevadensis* Eigenmann and Eigenmann. Pelvic fins may be reduced or absent. Several subspecies in various water holes in Nye County, Nevada and in San Bernardino County, California.

DEVILS HOLE CYPRINODON, *Cyprinodon diabolis* Wales. Smallest of all pupfish; pelvic fins absent. Devils Hole, Ashe Meadows, Nye County, Nevada.

SALT CREEK CYPRINODON, *Cyprinodon salinus* Miller. More slender than most pupfish. Salt Creek, Death Valley, California.

OWENS VALLEY CYPRINODON, *Cyprinodon radiosus* Miller. Owens Valley, California.

4b. Opercular opening closed by union of gill membrane to shoulder some distance above pectoral fin base about half way to upper corner of opercle.....................................*Floridichthys*
FLORIDA GOLDSPOTTED KILLIFISH, *Floridichthys carpio* (Gunther). Fig. 411. Light olive. Males with silvery sides and about 6 faint coppery cross bars; sides sprinkled with yellow spots; dorsal and anal fins finely speckled and margined with orange. Female with plain fins and with many yellow blotches. Humeral scale not enlarged. Length 3 inches. Brackish water from Key West to Texas.

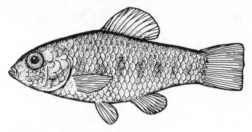

Figure 411

5a. Pelvic fins absent or undeveloped.................*Empetrichthys*
Dark brown above, lighter below and often somewhat mottled; fins dusky and may be speckled.

ASH MEADOWS SPRINGFISH, *Empetrichthys merriami* Gilbert. Fig. 412. Ash Meadows, Nye County, Nevada.

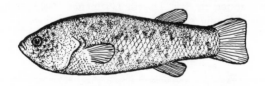

Figure 412

PAHRUMP SPRINGFISH, *Empetrichthys latos* Miller. Desert waterholes in Pahrump Valley, Nye County, Nevada.

5b. Pelvic fins present..**6**

6a. Teeth in more than one row; teeth in outer row may be large, and teeth in inner row or rows may be small......................**7**

6b. Teeth in a single row......................................**8**

7a. Less than 30 scales in body length; upper margin of gill membrane (opercle) joined to shoulder just above base of pectoral fin ....*Adinia*
DIAMOND KILLIFISH, *Adinia xenica* (Jordan and Gilbert). Fig. 413. Deep-bodied; scales in body length 25-28; more or less greenish with numerous cross bars; front of dorsal fin before front of pelvics. Length 2 inches. Brackish water from Florida to Texas. May enter freshwater.

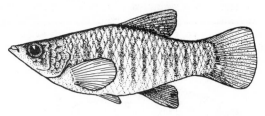

Figure 413

7b. More than 30 scales in body length; margin of gill membrane (opercle) not joined to shoulder just above base of pectoral fin but normal...*Fundulus*
Many species in this genus found in both salt and freshwater. See page 167 for key to species.

8a. Body short, depth goes 3¼ to 3¾ times in length........*Lucania*
RAINWATER FISH, *Lucania parva* (Baird and Girard). Fig. 414. Grayish and rather pale. Males with a large black spot at base of front of dusky orange dorsal fin; caudal fin edged with black. Females without dark edges on fins. Length 1½ inches. Swamps and brackish waters along Atlantic coast from Cape Cod southward to Mexico.

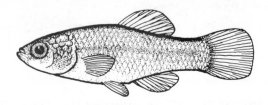

Figure 414

8b. Body more elongate, depth goes 4¼ to 5 times in length........9

9a. Body without any black lateral band; mouth short and nearly vertical; dorsal rays 7, anal rays 8.................Leptolucania
OCELLATED KILLIFISH, *Leptolucania ommata* (Jordan). Fig. 415. Straw color. Male with 5-6 dark cross bars on sides. Female with black spot large as pupil on side just in front of anal fin. Large spot at upper part of base of caudal fin. Length 1 inch. Swamps of Georgia and Florida.

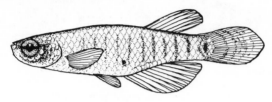

Figure 415

9b. Body with black lateral band extending through eye to snout; dorsal rays 9; anal rays 9..............................Chriopeops
REDTAIL KILLIFISH, *Chriopeops goodei* (Jordan). Fig. 416. Olivaceous with black lateral band ending in caudal spot; black ventral band from vent to base of caudal fin. Male with basal half of dorsal and anal fins black, outer half pale with black margin. Swamps of Georgia and Florida.

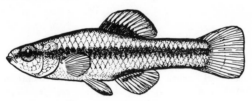

Figure 416

KILLIFISH, Genus *Fundulus*

1a. Front of dorsal fin above or before front of anal fin, never behind second ray of anal fin; dorsal fin with 10-17 rays..............2

1b. Front of dorsal fin behind second ray of anal fin; dorsal fin usually with 7-11 rays...10

2a. Front of dorsal fin distinctly before front of anal fin...........3

2b. Front of dorsal fin above or slightly behind front of anal fin......8

3a. Scales in body length 31-38; anal rays 10-12; body with or without cross bars..4

3b. Scales in body length 40-60; anal rays 11-14; body with many cross
bars 6

4a. Female (Fig. 417) with 2 or 3 more or less broken black horizontal
stripes; male (Fig. 418) with about 12 dark cross bars...........
..............STRIPED KILLIFISH, *Fundulus majalis* (Walbaum)

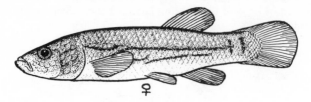

Figure 417

Olivaceous above, pale below; black spot in posterior part of
dorsal fin. Length 6 inches. Brackish water, sometimes entering freshwater, Cape Cod to Florida.

Figure 418

4b. Female plain or with cross bars only, no longitudinal stripes....5

5a. Males with dark cross bars. LONGNOSE KILLIFISH, *Fundulus
similis* (Baird and Girard)..............................Fig. 419
Males and females with 10 to 15 cross bars. Olivaceous above,
pale below. Males with large diffuse spot behind opercle. Young males
have black spot in posterior part of dorsal fin. Both sexes with black
spot (diffuse in adults) near base of caudal fin. Length 6 inches. Brackish water, may enter freshwater, Florida to Texas.

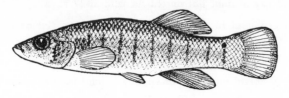

Figure 419

CALIFORNIA KILLIFISH, *Fundulus parvipinnis* Girard. Fig. 420. Males with about 20 cross bars. Females with obscure lateral shade posteriorly. Pale olive green, somewhat mottled above, pale below. Length 4 inches. Brackish water, southern California.

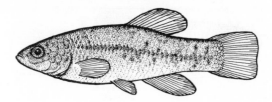

Figure 420

5b. Males with variable number of pale or silvery cross bars; females may be plain or may have about 15 dark cross bars; dorsal rays 11...............MUMMICHOG, *Fundulus heteroclitus* (Linnaeus)

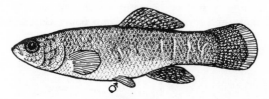

Figure 421

Dull green above, pale or yellowish below. Males (Fig. 421) with numerous white or yellow spots on sides; median fins dark; dorsal fin may have black blotch on last ray. Females (Fig. 422) with median fins plain. Length 5-6 inches. Brackish water, sometimes entering freshwater from Maine to Texas.

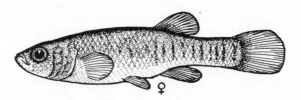

Figure 422

GULF KILLIFISH, *Fundulus grandis* Baird and Girard. Fig. 423. Very similar to the mummichog, but differs largely in having smaller and shorter fins. Length 6 inches. Marine and brackish water, Florida to Texas.

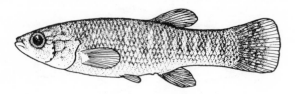

Figure 423

6a. Scales in body length 44-48; anal rays 11. Fig. 424..............
...............BANDED KILLIFISH, *Fundulus diaphanus* (LeSueur)
Olivaceous above with silvery sides. Marked with about 20 dark cross bars. Length 4 inches. Several subspecies widely distributed from North Dakota and Iowa to Quebec and South Carolina.

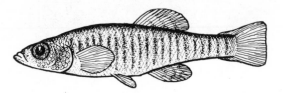

Figure 424

6b. Scales in body length over 50; anal rays over 11...............7

7a. Dorsal fin rays more than 15.................................
.................FLORIDA KILLIFISH, *Fundulus seminolis* Girard
Olive green or yellowish brown. Males with longitudinal streaks formed by spots on scales; dorsal and caudal fins with large dark spots on bars; outer part of caudal mostly black. Females (Fig. 425) and young with 12-14 rather faint cross bars. Length 3 inches. Florida.

Figure 425

7b. Dorsal fin rays less than 15. PLAINS KILLIFISH, *Fundulus kansae* Garman...Fig. 426
Greenish with silvery sides and belly; sides marked with numerous cross bars (14-20); black spot in front of dorsal fin. South Dakota and Wyoming south to Texas.

The ZEBRA KILLIFISH, *Fundulus zebrinus* Jordan and Gilbert, in Texas is very similar and may be a subspecies.

Figure 426

8a. Dorsal fin rays 13-15; anal fin rays 13-15.......................
...........................STUDFISH, *Fundulus catenatus* (Storer)
Bluish or green above and pale below with orange (male, Fig. 427) or brown (female, Fig. 428) spot on each scale; dorsal rays 14;

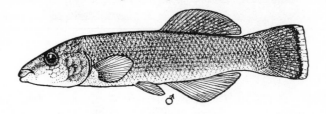

Figure 427

anal rays 14-15. Length 6-7 inches. Highlands of eastern Tennessee and the Ozarks of Missouri and Arkansas.

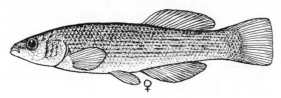

Figure 428

SOUTHERN STUDFISH, *Fundulus stellifer* (Jordan). Male bright blue above, silvery below; body and cheeks with irregularly scattered orange spots. Female with irregular brown dashes. Dorsal rays 13; anal rays 13. Length 4 inches. Alabama River system in Georgia and Alabama.

8b. Dorsal fin rays 10-11; anal fin rays 7-11......................9

9a. Scales in body length less than 40...........................
........**MARSH KILLIFISH,** *Fundulus confluentus* **Goode and Bean**
Brownish yellow. Male (Fig. 429) with many cross bars. Female
(Fig. 430) with sides marked with irregular dots; scales each with a dash
appearing as numerous lateral streaks. Dorsal fin with black spot
posteriorly; anal rays 7-9. Length 2½ inches. Coastal swamps Maryland to Florida and west to Louisiana.

Figure 429

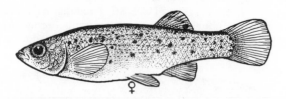

Figure 430

BAYOU KILLIFISH, *Fundulus pulvereus* (Evermann). Very similar
if not the same as the marsh killifish. Brackish water, Mobile, Alabama to Corpus Christi, Texas.

SALTMARSH KILLIFISH, *Fundulus jenkinsi* (Evermann). Pale olivaceous with minute brownish specks except on breast; no distinct cross
bars on sides. Males with 15-30 larger spots more or less in 2 rows
on sides which may form indistinct cross bars. Brackish water, Gulf
of Mexico, may enter freshwater.

SPECKLED KILLIFISH, *Fundulus rathbuni* Jordan and Meek. Similar
to blackspot killifish. Pale green with irregular dark spots over body;
anal rays 11. Young have pale cross bars. Length 2½ inches. Streams
of eastern North Carolina.

9b. Scales in body length about 42...............................
.....**WHITE STREAKED KILLIFISH,** *Fundulus albolineatus* **Gilbert**
Males dark brown with plumbeus sides, scale spots form inter-
rupted whitish streaks on sides. Females olivaceous and silvery below.
Scale rows form narrow black streaks. Length 3½ inches. Tennessee
River system.

10a. **Body either plain or with irregular spots. Fig. 431.............**
................**PLAINS TOPMINNOW,** *Fundulus sciadicus* Cope
Uniformly olivaceous punctulated with fine dots, belly pale; no bars
or streaks. Length 2½ inches. Missouri River system, South Dakota
to Colorado.

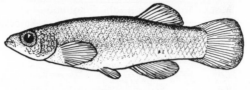

Figure 431

10b. **Body marked with either cross bars or longitudinal stripes.....11**

11a. **Body marked with single longitudinal stripe and random dots;
no cross bars; female rather plain. BLACKSTRIPE TOPMINNOW,**
Fundulus notatus (Rafinesque).........................**Fig. 432**
Brownish green with broad lateral band from snout to base of cau-
dal fin; spots on body and fins rather diffuse. Length 3½ inches.
Iowa to Ohio and south to parts of Tennessee, Mississippi, and Texas.

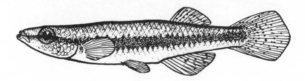

Figure 432

BLACKSPOTTED TOPMINNOW, *Fundulus olivaceous* (Storer). Fig.
433. Differs slightly from the preceding. Spots on body are smaller
and more concise. The predorsal and postdorsal stripe tends to be
lacking in adults although present at least as a row of spots in the preceding. Length 3½ inches. Oklahoma and Mississippi to western
Florida and Texas.

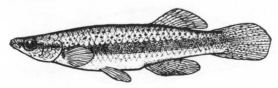

Figure 433

11b. Body marked with more than one longitudinal stripe or with cross bars..12

12a. Male with dark bar below eye...............................
...........STARHEAD TOPMINNOW, *Fundulus notti* (Agassiz)
Pale olive. Male (Fig. 434) with faint longitudinal streaks formed by dots on each scale, and about 10-12 cross bars. Female with longi-

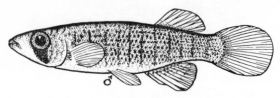

Figure 434

tudinal streaks, but cross bars faint or absent. Length 2½ inches. Several subspecies, Iowa to Ohio and South Carolina and south to Florida and Texas. (*F. n. lineolatus* Agassiz, Fig. 435).

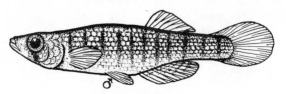

Figure 435

12b. Male without dark bar below eye...........................13

13a. Cross bars of male usually less than 12......................
.........GOLDEN TOPMINNOW, *Fundulus chrysotus* Holbrook
Olivaceous above, light below and flecked with gold. Male (Fig. 436) with 6-10 cross bars; median fins speckled. Female (Fig. 437) more

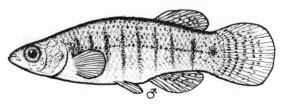

Figure 436

or less plain. Length 2½ inches. South Carolina to Louisiana and Oklahoma.

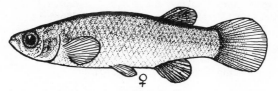

Figure 437

13b. Cross bars of both sexes usually more than 12. Fig. 438 . . . .
   BANDED or REDFIN KILLIFISH, *Fundulus cingulatus* **Valenciennes**
   Olivaceous. Male may have a few faint longitudinal streaks; body marked with 11-15 dark cross bars; belly orange and fins red. Females are more plain. Length 2½ inches. Coastal swamps and streams, North Carolina, Florida and Alabama.

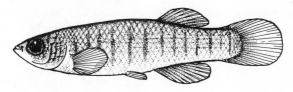

Figure 438

TOPMINNOW or LIVEBEARER FAMILY, Poeciliidae

The members of this family are small fishes restricted to the southern part of the United States and farther south. They are closely allied to the killifish family and are hard to separate on structural characters.

They differ from most other freshwater fishes of the United States in their mode of reproduction, the females giving birth to living young. The males bear an intromittent organ, the *gonopodium*, developed from the modified anal fin. Fertilization is internal, the male depositing sperm in the genital tract of the female. The female carries the developing eggs until they hatch internally, and the young emerge alive from the female.

They feed on minute insects and other small animal forms. They are usually found in shallow sloughs and pools. Many species are popular for aquaria.

1a. Origin of dorsal fin behind origin of anal fin; dorsal rays less than 12 2

1b. Origin of dorsal fin over or in front of the origin of the anal fin;
dorsal fin long and high, (very high in males of some species);
dorsal rays more than 12...........................*Mollienisia*
SAILFIN MOLLY, *Mollienisia latipinna* (LeSueur).......Fig. 439
Light olive green above and lighter below, somewhat spotted;
each scale with a spot. Dorsal fin marked with rows of spots; caudal
fin with entire black margin. Length about 3 inches. Common near
the coast from South Carolina into Mexico.

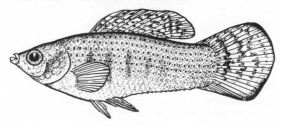

Figure 439

The AMAZON MOLLY, *Mollienisia formosa* (Girard) is a peculiar
form known only as females which mate with males of a wide number of other species. At present it is treated as a species presumably
of hybrid origin. Southern Texas into Mexico.

2a. Dorsal fin rays 7-8; anal fin rays 6-9; 24-28 scales in body length;
lower jaw slightly projecting................................3

2b. Dorsal fin rays 7-9; anal fin rays 8-10; 29-32 scales in body length;
dorsal fin far back, distance from origin to caudal fins is 1/2 distance to snout.......................................*Gambusia*
GAMBUSIA or the MOSQUITOFISH, *Gambusia affinis* (Baird and
Girard)...Figs. 440, 441

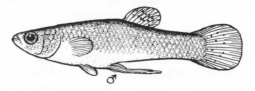

Figure 440

Light olive, each scale dark edged. Length about 1½ inches.
Widespread from southern Illinois and Indiana southward to Florida
and into Mexico. Introduced into California and elsewhere.
Gambusia nobilis (Baird and Girard) and *Gambusia gagei* Hubbs
are closely allied species reported from Texas.

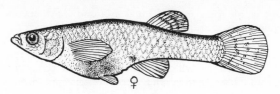

Figure 441

3a. Sides marked with lateral band and cross bars; black spot in dorsal and anal fins..*Heterandria*
LEAST KILLIFISH, *Heterandria formosa* Agassiz.........**Fig. 442**
Rather olivaceous. One of the smallest fishes in the United States. Length one inch. Swamps and ditches from South Carolina southward and along the Gulf coast.

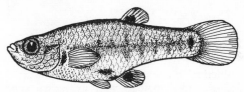

Figure 442

3b. Sides with faint lateral band and no cross bars; fins plain.....
....*Poeciliopsis*
Poeciliopsis occidentalis (Baird and Girard). Fig. 443. Brownish above dotted with black, silvery below. Length 2½ inches. Gila River system, Arizona into Mexico.

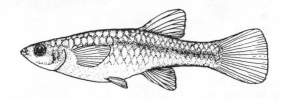

Figure 443

TROUTPERCH FAMILY, Percopsidae

These are small perch-like fishes with spiny fin rays but bearing a trout-like adipose fin. Only two species are in this family, one species being found in larger lakes and streams in the Great Lakes region and west to North Dakota and northward. Another species occurs in the Columbia River. They feed on small crustacea, aquatic insects, and other small aquatic animals.

1a. One very weak spine in anal fin; 2 thin and weak spines in dorsal fin. Fig. 444...
...........TROUT PERCH, *Percopsis omiscomaycus* (Walbaum)
Greenish yellow or straw color and mottled with a row of spots on the lateral line above which is another row of spots. Length 6 to 8 inches. Great Lakes region and upper Mississippi drainage northward.

Figure 444

1b. Two very stout spines in anal fin; 2 stout spines in dorsal fin. Fig. 445...SAND ROLLER, *Columbia transmontanus* (Eigenmann and Eigenmann)
Greenish yellow, sides mottled with numerous spots above and on the lateral line. Length about 6 inches. Lower Columbia River drainage.

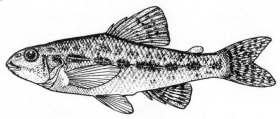

Figure 445

PIRATEPERCH FAMILY, Aphredoderidae

This family contains but one species, the PIRATEPERCH, *Aphredoderus sayanus* (Gilliams), Fig. 446, in the central Mississippi valley from southern Minnesota southward and along the coastal plain from New York southward to Texas.

The body is dark olive, somewhat speckled; with two dark bars at the base of the caudal fin and becomes quite irridescent during the spawning season. Length about 5 inches. The outstanding character is the location of the anus. This moves forward as the fish grows until it is located under the throat (jugular) of the adults. The lateral line on the sides is only slightly or partly developed in most mid-western specimens but those from the Atlantic coastal region show a much better developed lateral line.

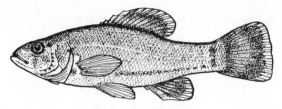

Figure 446

The pirateperch build a nest and both parents are claimed to guard the nest. They are predaceous, feeding mostly on aquatic insects and other small aquatic animals.

MULLET FAMILY, Mugilidae

This family contains the mullets which are found in the warmer seas over the world. Mullets are characterized by small weak mouths and by a small 4 spined dorsal fin considerably in advance of the soft portion of the dorsal fin. The pectorals are located high on the sides of the body. They may bear conspicuous adipose membranes over their eyes as in the herrings.

Several species of mullets enter freshwater in the southern United States. The COMMON MULLET, *Mugil cephalus* Linnaeus, Fig. 447, penetrates up the rivers of the Gulf states and in California. The writer has collected it in the Mississippi river over a hundred miles above the mouth. It may reach a length of 2 feet.

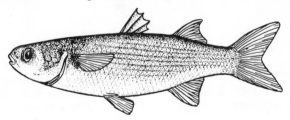

Figure 447

The WHITE MULLET, *Mugil curema* Valenciennes also penetrates into river mouths from Cape Cod to Texas. Several other species of mullets may stray into freshwater. The MOUNTAIN MULLET, *Agonostomus monticola* (Bancroft) found in the West Indies, occurs in small streams of eastern Florida. It is about 8 inches long. It resembles the common mullet, but lacks the adipose eyelids.

SILVERSIDES FAMILY, Atherinidae

The silversides are slender fishes, usually small and with a rather conspicuous silvery band on their sides. Many species occur in the warmer seas and several species occur in freshwater. The dorsal fin is divided into a small spinous portion and a larger soft-rayed portion which are widely separated.

The freshwater species are pale and rather transparent green in color with a wide silvery longitudinal band on each side. They seldom reach a length of more than 3 inches. They often swim in schools at the surface and may skip short distances out of the water. They spawn in the spring and produce eggs which have a sticky thread enabling them to float until the thread becomes attached to some object.

1a. **Scales with edges wrinkled or jagged**...........................
............SILVERFISH, *Membras vagrans* (Goode and Bean)
Greenish silver, with narrow lateral bands. Resembles the following species. Length 4 inches. Marine, enters freshwater along the Gulf of Mexico.

1b. **Scales with edges smooth**....................................2

2a. **Scales large, 38-40 in body length; jaws not prolonged into a beak.**
Fig. 448........MISSISSIPPI SILVERSIDES, *Menidia audens* Hay
Brackish water, ascending Mississippi river and connected waters as far north as Tennessee. It is very similar and closely related to the TIDEWATER SILVERSIDES, *Menidia beryllina* (Cope) which enters river mouths along the coasts of the Atlantic and the Gulf of Mexico.

Figure 448

2b. **Scales small, 76-80 in body length; jaws prolonged into a beak.**
Fig. 449........BROOK SILVERSIDES, *Labidesthes sicculus* (Cope)
Common in the lakes and larger streams of the upper Mississippi drainage and Great Lakes region south to Texas and Florida.

Figure 449

BASS FAMILY, Serranidae

This family is better known as a marine group as it contains many important marine fishes, such as sea bass, groupers, jewfishes, and others. Several species of this family are restricted to freshwater, and several marine species regularly enter freshwater. This family closely resembles the Sunfish Family to which the black basses belong, and is differentiated externally by several rather obscure characters. The freshwater species do not build nests, but spawn at random in the spring and give no care to the eggs or young. The dorsal fin is often completely divided, and the dorsal spinous portion is higher than in the sunfish family. Also, they have several skeletal differences and possess well-developed pseudobranchiae.

1a. Dorsal fins separate; soft anal rays 11 or 12; lower jaw projecting 2

1b. Dorsal fins joined; soft anal rays 8 to 10; jaws about equal....3

2a. Depth of body more than 1/3 standard length; 2nd anal spine about 1/3 length of head. Fig. 450.............................
.....................WHITE BASS, *Roccus chrysops* (Rafinesque)
Silvery color, sides with about 7 longitudinal stripes which may be broken. Reaches length of 18 inches. Minnesota east through lower Great Lakes and St. Lawrence drainage and south to northern Alabama and to Texas. Introduced elsewhere.

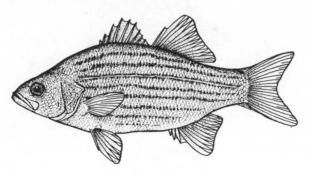

Figure 450

2b. Depth of body less than 1/3 standard length; second anal spine about 1/5 the length of the head. Fig. 451......................
.....................STRIPED BASS, *Roccus saxatilis* (Walbaum)

181

Back olivaceous; sides silvery or brassy, marked with about 7 dark longitudinal lateral stripes. Reaches large size in the sea, weighing over 100 pounds. Anadromous, entering streams of Atlantic coast. Introduced and common on Pacific coast.

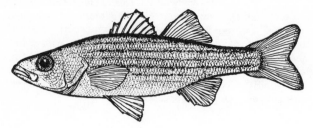

Figure 451

3a. **Sides with 7 longitudinal black stripes, those below lateral line broken under dorsal fin; longest dorsal spine more than 1/2 the length of the head. Fig. 452**..................................
.........................YELLOW BASS, *Morone interrupta* Gill
Brassy yellow. Length 18 inches. Southern Minnesota to Ohio and southward in Mississippi Valley.

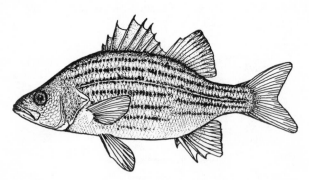

Figure 452

3b. **Sides nearly plain, may have faint light streaks; longest dorsal spine about 1/2 length of head. Fig. 453**.....................
....................WHITE PERCH, *Morone americana* (Gmelin)
Back olivaceous; sides more or less silvery. Length 14 inches. Marine, common along the Atlantic coast southward to South Carolina,

frequently entering rivers and connected bodies of waters. May become landlocked.

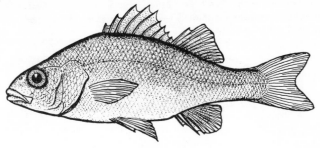

Figure 453

SUNFISH FAMILY, Centrarchidae

The sunfish family contains not only the sunfishes, but also the crappies and black basses. Most of these are either game or pan fishes. The members of this family were originally not found west of the Rocky Mountains except for the Sacramento Perch in the central valley of California. Many species of this family have been introduced all over the world.

The sunfishes, crappies and blackbasses prefer the warmer lakes and streams from southern Canada to the Gulf. They are all nesting fishes. The males scoop out a depression where one or more females deposit eggs. The males guard the eggs and the newly hatched young.

The members of this family closely resemble those of the perch family and the bass family. They differ in that the spinous and soft portions of the dorsal fin are united and confluent, except in the largemouth bass where a deep notch almost separates the two parts.

1a. Body elongated; depth goes about 3 times in standard length...2

1b. Body short and deep; depth goes less than 3 times in standard length 7

2a. Lateral line absent; dorsal fin not deeply notched; caudal fin rounded; scale rows less than 50, PYGMY SUNFISHES, *Elassoma*......3

2b. Lateral line developed and present; dorsal fin almost divided; caudal fin notched; lateral line scales more than 58................4

3a. Scale rows in body length 35 to 45; dorsal spines 5. Fig. 454....
............BANDED PYGMY SUNFISH, *Elassoma zonatum* Jordan
Olivaceous with about 11 vertical bars on sides; black spot size of eye on side under front of dorsal fin. Length 1½ inches. Southern Illinois to Texas and Georgia.

Figure 454

3b. Scale rows in body length 27 to 30; dorsal spines 3-4. Fig. 455...
.....EVERGLADES PYGMY SUNFISH, *Elassoma evergladei* Jordan
Olivaceous with variable markings. Length 1½ inches. Swamps of southern Georgia and Florida.

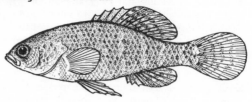

Figure 455

4a. Upper jaw extends past posterior margin of orbit; spinous dorsal fin separated from soft dorsal fin by a deep notch extending almost to base of fin. Fig. 456.................................
........LARGEMOUTH BASS, *Micropterus salmoides* (Lacépède)
Dark green above, sides and belly silvery; dark lateral band present, breaks up in old individuals. Length up to 20 inches or more. Southern Canada through Great Lakes drainage and south into Mexico; Virginia to Florida on Atlantic coast. Widely introduced elsewhere.

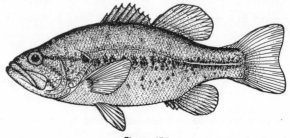

Figure 456

184

4b. Upper jaw does not extend to posterior margin of orbit; spinous dorsal fin incompletely separated by shallow notch from soft dorsal fin..5

5a. Body with a longitudinal stripe of connected black blotches on each side. Fig. 457...
..........SPOTTED BASS, *Micropterus punctulatus* (Rafinesque)
Greenish above, silvery below and somewhat mottled. Length up to 17 inches. Southern Illinois, Missouri, and Ohio southward to Texas and Gulf.

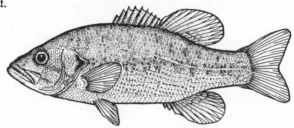

Figure 457

SUWANNEE BASS, *Micropterus notius* Bailey and Hubbs has markings similar to those of the spotted bass, but other characteristics similar to those of the smallmouth bass. Ichtucknee Springs, Columbia County, Florida.

TEXAS SPOTTED BASS, *Micropterus treculi* (Valliant and Boucourt). Regarded as a distinct species. Texas.

5b. Body without longitudinal lateral stripe; may be plain or with faint vertical bars 6

6a. Soft dorsal rays usually 13-15. Fig. 458.......................
..........SMALLMOUTH BASS, *Micropterus dolomieui* Lacépède
Greenish above, dusky silver below; each scale sometimes with a brassy spot. Length up to 18 inches. Minnesota to Quebec and south to Arkansas and northern Alabama. Widely introduced elsewhere.

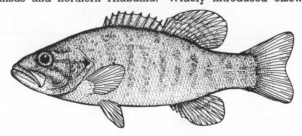

Figure 458

6b. Soft dorsal rays usually 12....................................
....REDEYE BLACK BASS, *Micropterus coosae* Hubbs and Bailey
Upland streams of Georgia and Alabama.

185

7a. Base of dorsal fin only slightly longer than anal fin...........8
7b. Base of dorsal fin much longer than base of anal fin........10
8a. Dorsal spines more than 10; anal spines usually 7 or 8. Fig. 459..
................FLIER, *Centrarchus macropterus* (Lacépède)
Body quite deep; greenish, each scale with a brown spot giving appearance of numerous rows of dots on sides. Length 6-7 inches. Virginia to Florida, and southern Illinois southward in Mississippi valley.

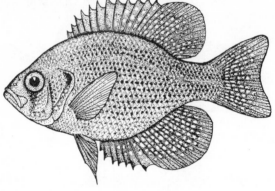

Figure 459

8b. Dorsal spines less than 10; anal spines usually 6..............9

9a. Distance from eye to front of dorsal fin base about equal to base of dorsal fin. Fig. 460...
...........BLACK CRAPPIE, *Pomoxis nigromaculatus* (LeSueur)
Silvery, mottled with dark green or black; vertical fins spotted. Length up to 12 inches. Upper Mississippi Valley and Great Lakes, southward to Florida and Texas. Widely introduced elsewhere.

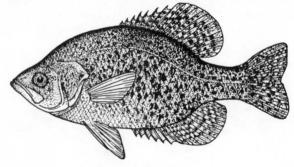

Figure 460

9b. Distance from eye to front of dorsal fin base greater than length of base of dorsal fin. Fig. 461................................
................WHITE CRAPPIE, *Pomoxis annularis* Rafinesque

Silvery white, mottled with dark green or black and with vertical bars on sides. Length up to 12 inches. Southern Minnesota and Great Lakes region south to Texas.

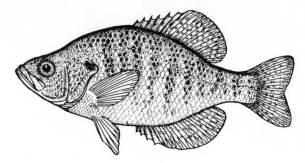

Figure 461

10a. Caudal fin more or less rounded..........................**11**

10b. Caudal fin more or less forked..........................**14**

11a. Scales cycloid; mouth large, maxillary extending behind middle of eye. Fig. 462....MUD SUNFISH, *Acantharchus pomotis* **(Baird)**
Dark greenish with 5 rather indistinct dark longitudinal bands along sides. Length up to 6 inches. Lowland streams, New York to South Carolina.

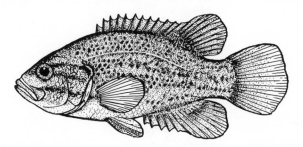

Figure 462

11b. Scales ctenoid; mouth small, maxillary not extending behind middle of eye..**12**

12a. Dorsal spines 10; front of dorsal fin black. Fig. 463..........
........**BLACKBANDED SUNFISH,** *Mesognistius chaetodon* **(Baird)**
Straw color, sides strongly banded with transverse bars, the bar behind the shoulder extending over the front of the dorsal fin. Length about 4 inches. Lowland streams from New Jersey to Florida.

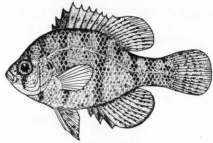

Figure 463

12b. Usually 9 dorsal spines; no black streak at front of dorsal fin..13
13a. Sides with 5 to 8 distinct crossbars; numerous pale or light blue
     spots on spiny part of dorsal fin. Fig. 464.....................
     ....BANDED SUNFISH, *Enneacanthus obesus* (Girard)
     Olivaceous, with purplish or golden spots on body and fins. Length
about 3 inches. Coastal lowlands, Massachusetts to Florida.

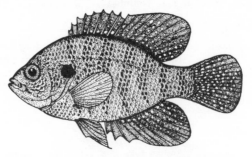

Figure 464

13b. Sides with indistinct crossbars; none or very few pale or light
     blue spots on spiny part of dorsal fin. Fig. 465................
     .....BLUESPOTTED SUNFISH, *Enneacanthus gloriosus* (Holbrook)
     Dark olivaceous with bright blue spots on sides and fins; pearly
spot in front of opercular spot. Length about 2¾ inches. Coastal lowlands, New Jersey to Florida.

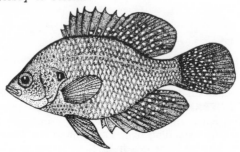

Figure 465

14a. Mouth large, maxillary extending behind middle of eye......15

14b. Mouth small, maxillary not extending behind middle of eye. The
SUNFISHES, *Lepomis*..17
The various species of this genus hybridize readily and the hy-
brids will not fit this key.

15a. Anal spines 3. Fig. 466.....................................
..............WARMOUTH, *Chaenobryttus coronarius* (Bartram)
Brassy—dark olive green, sometimes mottled; each scale with a
dark spot. Length up to 10 inches. Southern Minnesota and Great
Lakes region south to Texas and Florida.

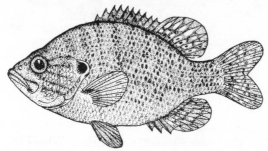

Figure 466

15b. Anal spines 5 to 8...16

16a. Longest anal spine about half the length of the spinous portion
of the anal fin; gill rakers 10. Fig. 467........................
................ROCKBASS, *Ambloplites rupestris* (Rafinesque)
Brassy—olivaceous and somewhat mottled; each scale with a dark
spot forming numerous rows of dots. Length up to 12 inches. Vermont
to Manitoba and south to the Gulf of Mexico. Several subspecies in
the south.

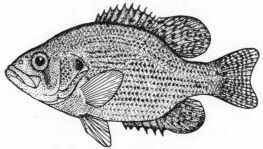

Figure 467

16b. Longest anal spine about equal to length of spinous part of anal fin; gill rakers 20. Fig. 468......................................
.........SACRAMENTO PERCH, *Archoplites interruptus* (Girard)
Dark back, silvery below with about 7 vertical bars on each side; bars are somewhat interrupted and irregular. Length up to 20 inches. Sacramento and San Joaquin River drainages, California.

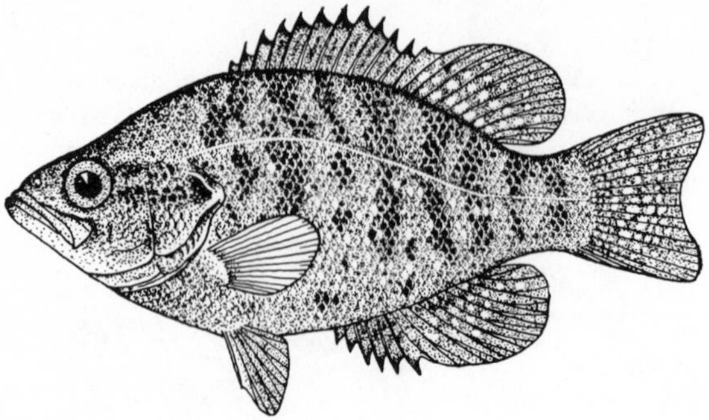

Figure 468

17a. Pectoral fin short and rounded, not reaching behind front of anal fin 18

17b. Pectoral fin long and pointed, reaching behind front of anal fin (except in immature individuals)...........................23

18a. Gill rakers long, length about 6 times width of base. Fig. 469.............................19

18b. Gill rakers short, length not more than 3 times width of base...............................20

Figure 469

19a. More than 45 scales in lateral line; lateral line complete; body oblong and stout. Fig. 470....................................
...............GREEN SUNFISH, *Lepomis cyanellus* Rafinesque
Brassy-green; opercular lobe dark with light bronze margin. Length about 6 inches. Minnesota and Great Lakes region south to Mexico, not east of the Alleghenies.

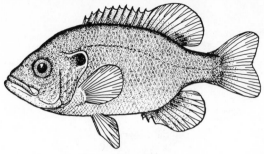

Figure 470

19b. Less than 40 lateral line scales; lateral line interrupted, many scales not pored; body rounded. Fig. 471.................... ....*Lepomis symmetricus* Forbes

Sides more or less barred; young have a dark ocellated spot at posterior base of dorsal fin; each scale marked with brown giving appearance of numerous rows of dots. Length about 3 inches. Southern Illinois to Louisiana and Texas.

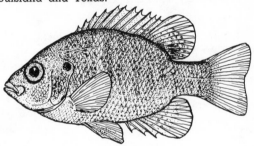

Figure 471

20a. Opercular lobe no longer than wide........................21
20b. Opercular lobe longer than wide except in immature individuals 22
21a. Opercular lobe soft, stiff only at base; length of gill rakers not more than 2 x width of base (Fig. 472); each scale pigmented at base. Fig. 473...
.............DOLLAR SUNFISH, *Lepomis marginatus* (Holbrook)

Olivaceous with orange on cheeks and belly, also numerous blue streaks; opercular lobe long and with pale greenish margin. Length 6-7 inches. Oklahoma to South Carolina and Florida.

Figure 472

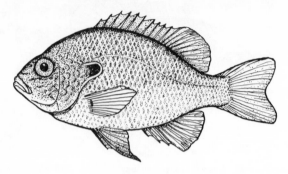

Figure 473

21b. Opercular lobe stiff most of its length; length of gill rakers about 3 x width of base (Fig. 474); each scale pigmented at base. Fig. 475.......SPOTTED SUNFISH, *Lepomis punctatus* (Valenciennes)

Olivaceous with numerous brown or black specks scattered over sides of body; opercular spot plain; opercular lobe rather short. Length about 6 inches. South Carolina to Florida. The subspecies *L. p. miniatus* Jordan has fewer specks and is common in Mississippi valley from southern Illinois to Texas.

Figure 474

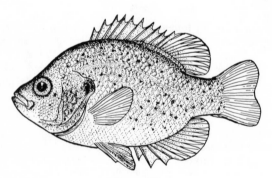

Figure 475

22a. Gill rakers short and knobby (Fig. 476), rather soft; opercular lobe as wide or wider than eye; lateral line scales 36-45. Fig. 477........LONGEAR SUNFISH, *Lepomis megalotis* (Rafinesque)

Brightly colored with orange spots and blue streaks; opercular lobe usually very long and may or may not have bluish colored margin. Length about 8 inches. Iowa to southern Quebec and south to South Carolina and southern Texas.

Figure 476

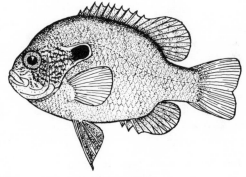

Figure 477

22b. Gill rakers short but hard or stiff (Fig. 478); opercular lobe not as wide as eye; lateral line scales 43-48. Fig. 479..............
...........YELLOWBELLY SUNFISH, *Lepomis auritus* (Linnaeus)

Olivaceous with orange belly, reddish spots and bluish streaks on body; opercular lobe often very long and usually plain. Length 8 inches. Maine to Florida and along coast of Texas.

Figure 478

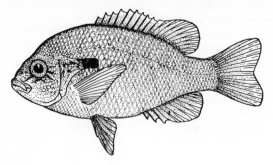

Figure 479

23a. Gill rakers long (Fig. 480), length
more than 2 x width of base.....24

23b. Gill rakers short (See Fig. 485), length
less than 2 x width of base.....25

Figure 480

24a. Lateral line scales more than 40; anal soft rays usually 10-12.
Fig. 481............BLUEGILL, *Lepomis macrochirus* Rafinesque
Olive green with some blue and orange on body; dark spot at
posterior base of dorsal fin; vertical bars on sides; opercular lobe solid
black; gill rakers long (See Fig. 480). Reaches length of over 10 inches.
Widespread from Minnesota to Lake Champlain and south to Florida
and Texas. Widely introduced elsewhere.

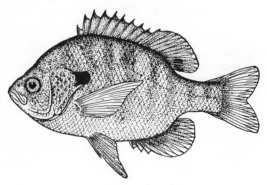

Figure 481

24b. Lateral line scales less than 40; anal soft rays 7-10. Fig. 482...
.........**ORANGESPOTTED SUNFISH,** *Lepomis humilis* (Girard)

Body brightly spotted with orange, opercular lobe with broad red or orange margin; pectoral fin about as long as head; gill rakers long (Fig. 483). Length about 4 inches. North Dakota to western Ohio and south to Texas and northern Alabama.

Figure 483

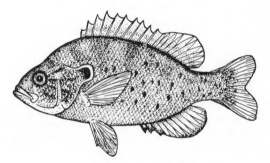

Figure 482

25a. Opercular lobe with a spot of orange or red in the lower part; pectoral fin 3 or more times in standard length. Fig. 484......
..................**PUMPKINSEED,** *Lepomis gibbosus* (Linnaeus)

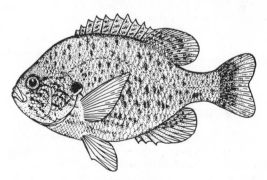

Figure 484

195

Very brightly colored with orange and some blue; gill rakers short (Fig. 485). Length over 8 inches. North Dakota east to Quebec and south to South Carolina, Ohio, and Iowa.

Figure 485

25b. Opercular lobe with broad red or orange margin below and behind; pectoral fins 3 or less times in standard length. Fig. 486...
..............REDEAR SUNFISH, *Lepomis microlophus* (Gunther)

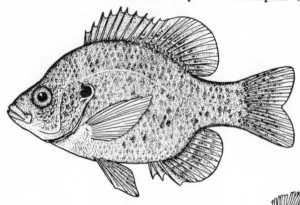

Figure 486

Olivaceous with yellow or orange breast; gill rakers short (Fig. 487). Length of 10 inches. Missouri to southern Indiana and south to Florida and Texas.

Figure 487

PERCH FAMILY, Percidae

This is an important group of freshwater fishes characterized by a dorsal fin which is completely divided into a spiny and a separate soft-rayed portion. The anal fin bears one or two spines. The family consists of three divisions or subfamilies: (1) Percinae, the perch; (2) Luciopercinae, the pikeperch and sauger; (3) the Etheostomatinae, the darters.

All members of this family spawn in the spring in a variety of ways. The perch string their eggs in gelatinous strings over the vegetation. The pikeperches deposit their eggs at random in shallow water. Some darters (logperch, Iowa darter, and least darter) do likewise, while others (rainbow darter) cover their eggs with gravel or sand. Some, such as the Johnny darter and the fantail darter, place their eggs on the underside of objects where they are cared for by the males. In many of the darters, the males assume brilliant colors in the spawning season.

All members of this family are predaceous, the larger species being highly piscivorous, and the smaller darters preying on minute insects and crustacea.

1a. Branchiostegal rays 5 or 6; pectoral fins larger than usual; upper jaw not extending to middle of eye; pseudobranchiae absent or poorly developed; small fishes, adults seldom exceeding 6 inches in length, usually much smaller.................................2

1b. Branchiostegal rays 7 or 8; pectoral fins normal size; upper jaw extending to or behind middle of eye; pseudobranchiae well developed; size usually large, adults more than 5 inches in length...4

2a. Depth of body goes 7 or more times in length and anal fin has only one spine; scales on trunk tend to be limited to middle of sides; may have several, although usually only one row of scales below lateral line anterior to anus except in crystal darter which has only the belly naked.........................*Ammocrypta*
Slender darters which are rather pellucid.

CRYSTAL DARTER, *Ammocrypta asprella* (Jordan).......Fig. 488
Lateral line scales 89-100; anal rays 12-14. Length 4-5 inches. Iowa to southern Ohio and south to Alabama and Oklahoma. Other members of this genus have less than 80 lateral line scales and less than 10 anal rays. They seldom reach more than 2 inches in length.

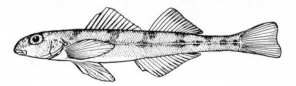

Figure 488

NORTHERN SAND DARTER, *Ammocrypta pellucida* (Baird). **Fig. 489**
Cheeks and opercles scaly; peduncle entirely scaled; anterior number of scale rows irregular and mostly confined to above lateral line. Rows of dots on sides well defined and not connected. Great Lakes and Ohio River drainages.

Figure 489

WESTERN SAND DARTER, *Ammocrypta clara* Jordan and Meek.
. . . . **Fig. 490**
Cheeks and opercles more or less scaly; peduncle entirely scaled; scales on trunk confined anteriorly to several rows above lateral line. Southern Minnesota to Indiana and southward to Texas.

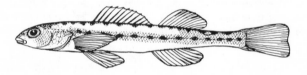

Figure 490

ARKANSAS SAND DARTER, *Ammocrypta vivax* Hay . . . . . **Fig. 491**
Cheeks and opercles scaly; peduncle entirely scaled; anteriorly scales cover most of sides above lateral line, covering back in front of dorsal fin. Row of spots on sides diffuse and not connected. Oklahoma and Mississippi to Texas.

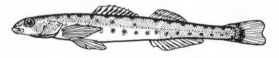

Figure 491

SOUTHERN SAND DARTER, *Ammocrypta beani* Jordan . . . **Fig. 492**
Cheeks and opercles without scales; scales on trunk and peduncle limited to several rows on and above lateral line. No row of spots on

sides; dark blotch in anterior part of spinous dorsal fin. Coastal streams, Mississippi to Florida.

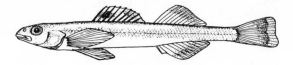

Figure 492

2b. **Depth of body usually goes less than 7 times in body length and anal fin has one or two spines, or if depth goes over 7 times in body length, anal fin has 2 spines; scales on trunk covering most of body (nape may be naked); sides well scaled below lateral line, although belly may be more or less naked in some species....3**

3a. **Belly may be naked except for a row of enlarged or modified scales on the midventral line (Fig. 493) or belly may be more or less scaled with one or more modified scales between the pelvic**

Figure 493

fins (Fig. 494); area of anal fin usually as large as area of soft dorsal fin; pelvic fins in most species widely separated, space between them usualy at least 3/4 as wide as base of either fin.................*Percina* Many species in this genus which includes those formerly in *Hadropterus* and several other genera. See page 201.

Figure 494

3b. **Belly usually scaled, but if naked no midventral row of modified scales present or no modified scales present between pelvic fins (Fig. 495); space between pelvic fins usually less than 3/4 as wide as the base of either fin (except in several species); area of anal fin usually less than area of soft dorsal fin ....*Etheostoma*** Many species in this genus. See page 207.

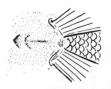

Figure 495

199

4a. Body with prominent cross bars (may be faint in young); pelvic fins close together, space between less than width of base of either fin; without oversize or fang-like teeth (canines)............*Perca*

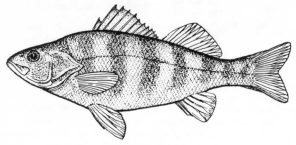

Figure 496

YELLOW PERCH, *Perca flavescens* (Mitchill)............Fig. 496
Widely distributed from northern Kansas to Ohio and South Carolina and northward into Canada. Widely introduced elsewhere.

4b. Body without strong cross bars; pelvic fins widely separated by space equal to width of base of either fin; many elongated or fang-like (canine) teeth..................................*Stizostedion*
PIKEPERCH or WALLEYE, *Stizostedion vitreum* (Mitchill)..Fig. 497
Lower lobe of caudal fin whitish; dark spot at posterior end of spinous dorsal fin; no black spot on basal part of pectoral fin; 3 or 4 pyloric caeca (finger-like structures where intestine leaves stomach). Reaches length of 36 inches. Tennessee River drainage northward into southern Canada and northwestward to Great Slave Lake.

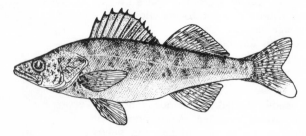

Figure 497

SAUGER, *Stizostedion canadense* (Smith)...............Fig. 498
Lower lobe of caudal fin not whitish; no dark spot at posterior base of spinous dorsal fin; black spot on basal portion of pectoral fin; 5-6 pyloric caeca. Reaches length of about 15 inches. Vermont,

Tennessee to Arkansas and Wyoming and northward into southern Canada.

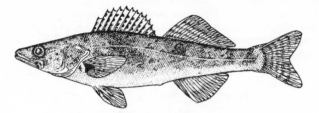

Figure 498

GENUS *PERCINA*

1a. Snout extends before upper lip; sides marked with numerous cross bars or with spots...
..............LOG PERCH *Percina caprodes* (Rafinesque). **Fig. 499.**
Yellowish with sides marked by many vertical bars. Belly naked with a midventral row of modified scales. Reaches a length of 6 inches. Several subspecies, Minnesota to Vermont and south to Mississippi and Texas.

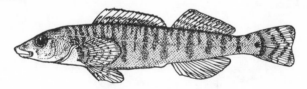

Figure 499

Percina rex (Jordan and Evermann). Similar to log perch except sides are marked with rows of spots. Headwaters of Roanoke River, Virginia.

1b. Snout does not extend before upper lip; sides usually marked with longitudinal row of large blotches which tend to be confluent along the lateral line...2

2a. Premaxillaries usually protractile, separated from snout by a groove, in some a slight fleshy bridge or frenum may be hidden in the groove...3

2b. Premaxillaries not protractile, connected with snout by a smooth fleshy bridge or frenum..5

3a. Spiny dorsal fin separated from soft dorsal fin by a wide space...
........CHANNEL DARTER, *Percina copelandi* (Jordan). Fig. 500.
Some specimens may show a frenum or fleshy bridge connecting premaxillaries to snout. Brownish with row of small blotches on sides and a tiny black spot at base of caudal fin. Length 2½-3 inches. Eastern Michigan to upper St. Lawrence drainage and south on western side of Appalachians to northern Alabama and to Oklahoma.

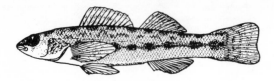

Figure 500

3b. Spiny dorsal fin separated by only a deep notch from soft dorsal fin 4

4a. Cheeks scaled ....
...........RIVER DARTER, *Percina shumardi* (Girard). Fig. 501.
Rather dark with 8-10 lateral blotches. Length 3 inches. Southern Manitoba and western Ontario to Ohio and south to Oklahoma and northern Alabama.

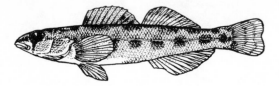

Figure 501

4b. Cheeks naked ....STAR-
GAZING DARTER, *Percina uranidea* (Jordan and Gilbert). Fig. 502.
Greenish olive with 9-10 lateral spots and a small black spot at base of caudal fin. Length 2½ inches. Southern Indiana and southern Missouri south to Arkansas and western Florida.

Figure 502

5a. Belly scaled and with no midventral row of modified scales, but with scales like those of the sides; a more or less modified scale present between the pelvic fins. (See Fig. 494)...............6

5b. Belly more or less naked and with a midventral row of enlarged or modified scales or with a modified scale between the pelvic fins. (See Fig. 494)...7

6a. Snout short and blunt; gill membranes scarcely connected......
........ORANGE DARTER, *Percina aurantiaca* (Cope). Fig. 503.
Olive above and yellowish below; a row of confluent blotches with row of dots above along each side; a black spot at base of caudal fin. Males with much orange. Length 5-6 inches. Headwaters of Tennessee River.

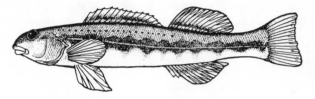

Figure 503

BLUFSTRIPE DARTER, *Percina cymatotaenia* (Gilbert and Meek)
....Fig. 504
Yellowish green above and heavily speckled, and with a rather dark longitudinal band on each side and a small black spot at base of caudal fin. Length 4-5 inches. Western Kentucky, southern Missouri and Arkansas.

Figure 504

6b. Snout long and sharp; gill membranes connected.............
..........OLIVE DARTER, *Percina squamata* (Gilbert and Swain)
Yellowish olive with 10 dusky blotches along each side and with a diffuse blotch with a small black dot behind it at the base of the caudal fin. Conspicuous black humeral spot present. Length 5 inches. Headwaters of the Tennessee River.

7a. Gill membranes not closely
connected. Fig. 505........8

7b. Gill membranes closely connected. Fig. 506..........11

8a. Cheeks entirely naked......9

8b. Cheeks scaled more or less.10

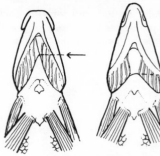

Figure 505   Figure 506

9a. Scales in lateral line or body length more than 70.............
....BIGHEADED DARTER, *Percina macrocephala* (Cope). Fig. 507.
Pale brown with about 9 confluent spots along each side; small
black spot at base of caudal fin. Length 6 inches. Pennsylvania
southward on west slope of Appalachians to Georgia.

Figure 507

9b. Scales in lateral line or body length less than 70.............
..GILT DARTER, *Percina evides* (Jordan and Copeland). Fig. 508.
More or less olivaceous and bronze with about 7 vertically elongated blotches more or less confluent along the lateral line and confluent
above with the dorsal blotches. Length 4 inches. Eastern Minnesota
through the Ohio drainage to New York and south to Oklahoma and
northern Georgia.

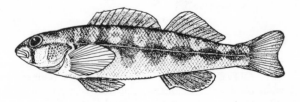

Figure 508

204

SHIELD DARTER, *Percina peltata* (Stauffer).............**Fig 509**
Pale yellowish with dark saddles on back and with about 6 square blotches which are sometimes confluent on each side. Length 3 inches. Pennsylvania to South Carolina on east side of Appalachians.

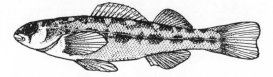

Figure 509

Percina crassa (Jordan and Brayton).
Yellowish with about 6 diffuse and more or less confluent blotches alternating with dark bands on each side. Males with 2 yellow spots at base of caudal fin. Length about 3 inches. Virginia to South Carolina.

ROANOKE DARTER, *P. crassa roanoka* (Jordan and Jenkins)....
....**Fig. 510**
Is very similar. Roanoke River, Virginia.

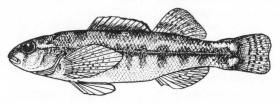

Figure 510

10a. Scales in lateral line or body length usually more than 70.....
.....**BLACKSIDE DARTER, *Percina maculata* (Girard). Fig. 511.**
Pale yellowish with row of 5-6 black and rather elongated blotches on each side and a small black spot at base of caudal fin. Length 3 inches. Southern Manitoba and Ontario to New York and southward east of the Appalachians to northern Alabama and Oklahoma.

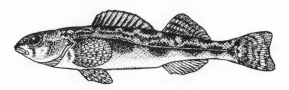

Figure 511

Percina pantherina (Moore and Reeves).
Very similar to the blackside darter but has more than 80 scale rows, and is more spotted. Little River System, western Arkansas and eastern Oklahoma.

10b. Scales in lateral line or in body length usually less than 70....
BLACKBANDED DARTER, *Percina nigrofasciata* **(Agassiz). Fig. 512.**
Olivaceous above and pale below with a row of 10-11 elongated diamond-shape blotches along each side, no bar below the eye. Length 5 inches. Coastal streams, South Carolina to Louisiana.

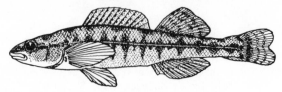

Figure 512

BRONZE DARTER, *Percina palmaris* **(Bailey).**
Yellowish brown above and dull olivaceous below with 8-10 dark vertical bars along each side; no dark bar under eye. Coosa-Alabama River System, Alabama and Georgia.
Percina notogramma (Raney and Hubbs).
Markings are similar to those of the blackside darter and the shield darter but has fewer scales in the lateral line and differs in the markings of the back, the mid-dorsal blotches seldom contact laterally with loops as in the related forms. Tributaries of Chesapeake Bay and south to the James River in Virginia.

11a. Cheeks usually naked...... *Percina crassa* **(Jordan and Brayton)**
Specimens with gill membranes more closely connected will key here. (See couplet 9b.)

11b. Cheeks more or less scaled................................12
12a. Scales along lateral line or body length less than 70; snout blunt
..............DUSKY DARTER, *Percina sciera* **(Swain). Fig. 513.**
Yellowish olive; each side with about 7 confluent blotches and with a small black spot at base of caudal fin. Length 5 inches. Indiana southward to Gulf and Texas.

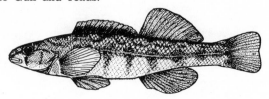

Figure 513

RIVER DARTER, *Percina shumardi* (Girard) ....
...................................(See Fig. 501, couplet 4a.)
Specimens with an apparent frenum will key here.

12b. **Scales along lateral line or in body length more than 70; snout long and sharp.**...
SLENDERHEAD DARTER, *Percina phoxocephala* (Nelson). Fig. 514.
Yellowish brown with 9-10 quadrate blotches along lateral line, ending in a small black spot at base of caudal fin. Length 6 inches. Minnesota to western Pennsylvania and south to Tennessee and Oklahoma.

Figure 514

LONGNOSE DARTER, *Percina nasuta* (Bailey).
Very similar to the slenderhead darter. Yellowish with 10-14 vertically elongate blotches along lateral line and a small black spot at base of caudal fin; no dark bar under eye. White River System, Arkansas and Poteau Rivers, Oklahoma.

Percina oxyrhyncha (Hubbs and Raney).
Similar in appearance to the slenderhead and the bigheaded darter. Cheat and New Rivers, Virginia and West Virginia.

OLIVE DARTER, *Percina squamata* (Gilbert and Swain).
Specimens with belly partly naked will key here. (See couplet 6b.)

GENUS *ETHEOSTOMA*

1a. **Body depth goes about 7 times in body length; back naked from middle of first dorsal fin forward.**...........................
........GLASSY DARTER, *Etheostoma vitreum* (Cope). Fig. 515.
Body very slender and pellucid; belly mostly naked except for a few scales between pelvic fins. Length 2 inches. Maryland to North Carolina.

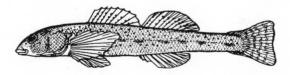

Figure 515

1b. Body depth goes less than 7 times in body length; back either entirely scaled or naked only in front of first dorsal fin.........2

2a. Premaxillaries protractile, separated from snout by a complete groove 3

2b. Premaxillaries not protractile, not entirely separated from snout by a groove, but connected anteriorly by a fleshy bridge......8

3a. Anal spines usually 2.......................................4

3b. Anal spines usually 1, first soft ray may resemble a spine as it is slender and unbranched, but it is jointed...................7

4a. Gill membranes only slightly connected across isthmus. Fig. 516.

SPECK DARTER, *Etheostoma stigmaeum* (Jordan). ....Fig. 517

Olivaceous and speckled with about 8 "W" shape blotches on each side. Length 2½ inches. Southeastern Oklahoma, Arkansas, and Tennessee to Georgia and Louisiana.

Figure 516

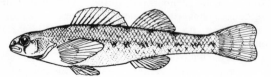

Figure 517

WACCAMAW DARTER, *Etheostoma perlongum* (Hubbs and Raney). Closely resembles the Johnny darter, but is more slender and has over 60 lateral line scales. Length 3 inches. Lake Waccamaw, Columbus County, North Carolina.

4b. Gill membranes closely united across isthmus (Fig. 518) 5

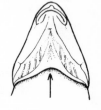

Figure 518

5a. Snout broadly rounded and bulges anteriorly, overhanging the premaxillaries or upper jaw....................................
GREENSIDE DARTER, *Etheostoma blennioides* **Rafinesque. Fig. 519.**
Body olivaceous; sides marked with series of "U" shape blotches. Length 4 inches. Michigan and Illinois to Pennsylvania and south to Alabama and Texas.

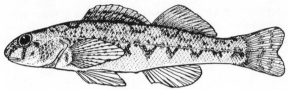

Figure 519

TENNESSEE SNUBNOSE DARTER, *Etheostoma simoterum* **(Cope).** ....Fig. 520
Light green above, yellowish below, with more or less confluent blotches along lateral line. Length 3 inches. Headwaters of Cumberland and Tennessee Rivers.

Figure 520

CUMBERLAND SNUBNOSE DARTER, *Etheostoma atripinne* **(Jordan).**
Body olivaceous with about 11 bar-like blotches along each side. Length 3 inches. Headwaters of the Green, Cumberland, and Tennessee Rivers.
5b. Snout more or less pointed and not greatly overhanging........6

6a. Snout shorter than diameter of eye.....................**WEED DARTER,** *Etheostoma podostemone* **Jordan and Jenkins. Fig. 521.**
Grayish brown with sides marked by row of "W" shape blotches. Length 3 inches. Headwaters of Roanoke River, Virginia.

Figure 521

6b. Snout as long as the diameter of eye.........................
.................ROCK DARTER, *Etheostoma longimanum* Jordan
Grayish brown with sides marked by longitudinal row of "W"
shape blotches. Length 3 inches. Headwaters of James River, Virginia.

7a. Lateral line complete; bar extending forward from eye is broken
on tip of snout...
......JOHNNY DARTER, *Etheostoma nigrum* Rafinesque. Fig. 522.
Grayish brown with sides marked by longitudinal row of "W"
shape blotches. Length 3 inches. Several subspecies, widespread
through upper Mississippi valley, Great Lakes drainage, and Atlantic
drainage south to northern Florida.

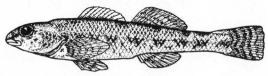

Figure 522

7b. Lateral line is incomplete, extending only a short distance; bar
extending forward from eye is continuous around snout........
BLUNTNOSE DARTER, *Etheostoma chlorosomum* (Hay). Fig. 523.
Grayish brown, sides marked with longitudinal row of "W" shape
blotches. Length 3 inches, southern Minnesota and Indiana to Alabama
and Texas.

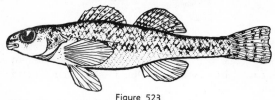

Figure 523

8a. Lateral line present, may be complete or incomplete..........9

8b. Lateral line entirely absent...................................34

9a. Lateral line complete or lacking only on the last 5 or 6 scales..10

9b. Lateral line incomplete, usually not extending beyond posterior
end of soft dorsal fin.......................................23

10a. Gill membranes more or less closely united across isthmus. (See
Fig. 518) 11

10b. Gill membranes not united or very slightly united across isthmus.
(See Fig. 516)...18

11a. Interspace between pelvic fins very narrow.............GOLD-
STRIPE DARTER, *Etheostoma parvipinne* Gilbert and Swain. Fig. 524.
Olivaceous, sides with about 10 cross bars, usually speckled and
with 3 or 4 distinct spots across base of caudal fin. Length 2½ inches.
Tennessee and Alabama west to Oklahoma and Texas.

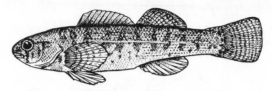

Figure 524

11b. Interspace between pelvic fins almost as wide as base of fin...12

12a. Dorsal spines 12 or more.....................................
..VARIEGATED DARTER, *Etheostoma variatum* Kirtland. Fig. 525.
Dusky green above, light below; sides with 6 or 7 cross bars posteriorly. Spring males very brilliant with vertical orange bars on sides
and orange on belly. Length 3½ inches. Ohio River drainage, exclusive of upper Tennessee, Kanawha, Wabash, and Kentucky River
systems.

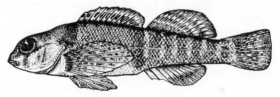

Figure 525

OSBURNS DARTER, *Etheostoma osburni* (Hubbs and Trautman)..
....Fig. 526
Dusky green above, light below with 9-11 blotches or bars on sides.
Similar to variegated darter. Length 4 inches. Upper Kanawha River
drainages, Virginia and West Virginia.

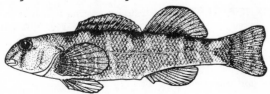

Figure 526

211

KANAWHA DARTER, *Etheostoma kanawhae* **(Raney).**
Similar to variegated darter, but breast is naked. Has fewer scales in lateral line (48-57) than Osburns darter (59-70). Length 3½ inches. New River drainage, Virginia and West Virginia.

CAROLINA GREENSIDE DARTER, *Etheostoma gutselli* **(Hildebrand)**
....**Fig. 527**
Brownish above, sides somewhat mottled and with 7 dark cross bars. Length 3½ inches. Tuckaseegee River, North Carolina.

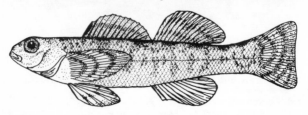

Figure 527

WELLBANDED DARTER, *Etheostoma euzonum* **(Hubbs and Black).**
Olivaceous with 7-8 vertical blotches or bars on sides. Similar to variegated darter. Length 3 inches. White River system, southeastern Missouri and northern Arkansas.

BLENNY DARTER, *Etheostoma blennius* **Gilbert and Swain. Fig. 528.**
Light olivaceous with dark oblique bars on sides. Length 3 inches. Upper tributaries of Tennessee River.

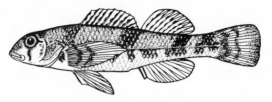

Figure 528

SWANNANOA DARTER, *Etheostoma swannanoa* **Jordan and Evermann**................................**(See Fig. 534, couplet 16b.)**
Individuals with more than 12 dorsal spines will key here.

12b. **Dorsal spines usually less than 12**............................13

13a. **Cheeks and opercles, both or only one scaled**................14

13b. **Cheeks and opercles practically naked, may have 3-5 scales**...15

14a. Cheeks naked, opercle scaled. *Etheostoma fricksium* Hildebrand.
....Fig. 529
Brownish above, sides with dark blotches. Length 2½ inches.
Savannah River, South Carolina and Georgia.

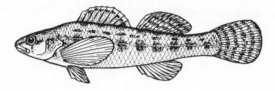

Figure 529

Etheostoma juliae Meek.............(See Fig. 561, couplet 33b.)
Individuals with rather complete lateral line will key here.

14b. Cheeks and opercles usually entirely scaled.................
..........BANDED DARTER, *Etheostoma zonale* (Cope). Fig. 530.
Olivaceous above, yellowish below; sides with brownish spots
along lateral line and 8 narrow bands encircling belly. Length 3 inches.
Southern Minnesota to Ohio and western New York and south to
Alabama and Arkansas.

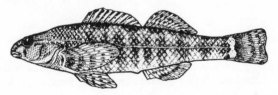

Figure 530

BLACKSIDE SNUBNOSE DARTER, *Etheostoma duryi* Henshall.
Dark greenish above, belly pale or orange; sides with 10 quad-
rate blotches along lateral line. Length 2-3 inches. Upper Tennessee
River drainage.

TENNESSEE SNUBNOSE DARTER, *Etheostoma simoterum* (Cope)
....(See Fig. 520, couplet 5a.)
Individuals with an apparent frenum will key here.

15a. Scale rows in lateral line 48 or more........................16

15b. Scale rows in lateral line less than 48......................17

16a. Anal soft rays 7-8 .... **HARLE-QUIN DARTER,** *Etheostoma histrio* Jordan and Gilbert. **Fig. 531.**
Dark green with alternating blotches along sides; belly naked.
Length 2 inches. Southern Indiana and Kentucky to southern Oklahoma.

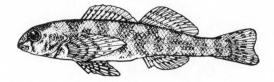

Figure 531

Etheostoma rupestre **Gilbert and Swain** .... **Fig. 532**
Greenish; sides marked with numerous small blotches, sometimes
"W" shape, above and below lateral line. Length 2 inches. Alabama.

Figure 532

16b. Anal soft rays 9 or more .... **SWANNANOA DAR-TER,** *Etheostoma swannanoa* Jordan and Evermann. **Fig. 533.**
Dusky green, sides more or less mottled; 8-9 blotches along lateral
line. Length 3 inches. Upper tributaries of the Tennessee River.

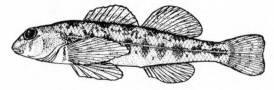

Figure 533

MISSOURI SADDLED DARTER, *Etheostoma tetrazonum* (Hubbs and Black).
Similar to variegated darter. Olivaceous light brown below with
4 dark saddles on back extending down almost to lateral line and
with 9-10 blotches along the side. Big Niangua River and Gasconade
River, Missouri.

17a. Pectoral fins no longer than head................SEAGREEN
DARTER, *Etheostoma thalassinum* (Jordan and Brayton). Fig. 534.
Dull greenish above and light below, sides with blotches. Males
with 6-9 blue green vertical bars on side. Length 2½ inches. Santee
River drainage, North and South Carolina.

Figure 534

Etheostoma mariae (Fowler)............................Fig. 535
Dull brownish above and light below; all fins reddish. Length
2¾ inches. Cape Fear River drainage, North Carolina.

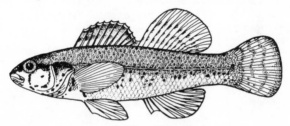

Figure 535

Etheostoma inscriptum (Jordan and Brayton).
Olivaceous with about six blotches along each side. Males with
a red spot on each scale, giving appearance of longitudinal lines.
Length 2½ inches. Georgia.

17b. Pectoral fins much longer than head.........................
......BLENNY DARTER, *Etheostoma blennius* Gilbert and Swain
Light olivaceous with dark oblique bars on sides. Length 3 inches.
Upper tributaries of Tennessee River. (See Fig. 528, couplet 12a.)

18a. Humeral region with large black humeral scale.............
................JORDANS DARTER, *Etheostoma jordani* Gilbert
Olivaceous with 8-10 cross bars on each side. Male with numerous longitudinal lines on sides similar to redline darter. Length 3
inches. Alabama River system in Georgia and Alabama.

REDFIN DARTER, *Etheostoma whipplei* (Girard)................
..................................(See Fig. 557, couplet 32a.)
Individuals with almost complete lateral line will key here.

**18b. Humeral region without an enlarged black scale, may have an
enlarged but not very dark scale or a faint spot**............19

215

19a. Head short, snout abruptly decurved.........................
    BLUEBREASTED DARTER, *Etheostoma camurum* (Cope). **Fig. 536.**
    Brownish and green, vertical fins edged with black. Males with
rich blue breasts and with red dots on sides. Length 2½ inches. Ohio
River drainage to North Carolina.

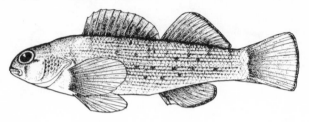

Figure 536

COOSA DARTER, *Etheostoma coosae* (Fowler)..........Fig. 537
    Light brown above and light below; sides mottled and with irregu-
lar vertical bands or blotches along lateral line. Length 2 inches.
Coosa River, Georgia and Alabama.

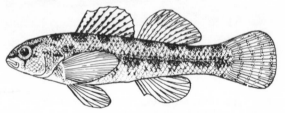

Figure 537

19b. Head rather long and pointed, snout not decurved..........20

20a. Scale rows in body length more than 70.............**NIANG-**
    UA DARTER, *Etheostoma nianguae* Gilbert and Meek....Fig. 538
    Olivaceous with 8-9 "U" shape bars on each side, 2 black spots
at base of caudal fin. Length 4 inches. Niangua and Gasconade River
drainages, Missouri.

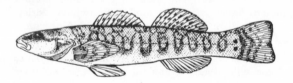

Figure 538

20b. Scale rows in body length less than 70....................21

21a. Scale rows in body length less than 50.......................
....REDLINE DARTER, *Etheostoma ruflineatum* (Cope) **Fig. 539.**
Greenish with 8 faint cross bars. Males with spots on each scale
forming a series of longitudinal lines along sides. Length 3 inches.
Tributaries of upper Tennessee, Cumberland, and Green Rivers.

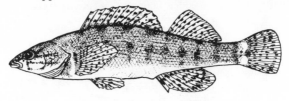

Figure 539

RAINBOW DARTER, *Etheostoma caeruleum* Storer.............
...................................(See **Fig. 550, couplet 29b**)
Individuals with rather complete lateral lines will key here.
Etheostoma fricksium Hildebrand......(See **Fig. 529, couplet 14a.**)
Individuals with gill membranes very slightly connected will key
here.

MUD DARTER, *Etheostoma asprigene* (Forbes)........... **Fig. 540**
Brownish above with about 9 squarish bar-like blotches on each
side. Lateral line usually incomplete. Individuals with more complete
lateral line will key here. Length 2 inches. Minnesota to Indiana and
south to Mississippi and Texas.

Figure 540

GULF DARTER, *Etheostoma swaini* (Jordan).............**Fig. 541**
Resembles mud darter, but lateral line is complete or almost complete. Scale spots form numerous irregular longitudinal streaks on
sides. Length 2½ inches. Gulf drainage, eastern Louisiana to Florida.

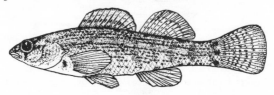

Figure 541

21b. Scale rows in body length more than 55................22

22a. Sides marked with blotches and with more or less fine horizontal
lines ....

SPOTTED DARTER, *Etheostoma maculatum* Kirtland. **Fig. 542.**
Dark olivaceous with a blue throat; scales on sides with spots giving appearance of numerous fine lines. Males with red spots and
about 10 vertical bars on sides. Length 2½ inches. Ohio to Northern
Alabama.

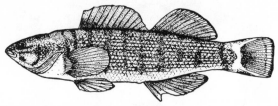

Figure 542

ASHY DARTER, *Etheostoma cinereum* Storer............**Fig. 543**
Yellowish brown with 10-12 dark oblong blotches on sides. Scale
spots form several longitudinal lines above lateral line. Length 4 inches.
Tributaries of upper Tennessee River.

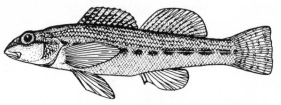

Figure 543

22b. Sides marked with "U" shape bars..........................
ARROW DARTER, *Etheostoma sagitta* (Jordan and Swain). **Fig. 544.**
Dusky green with about 9 "U" shape bars on sides. Length 3
inches. Tributaries of upper Cumberland River, Kentucky.

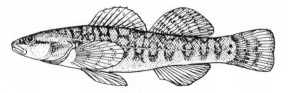

Figure 544

KENTUCKY DARTER, *Etheostoma spilotum* Gilbert.
Very similar to the arrow darter if not the same. Kentucky River,
Kentucky.

23a. Lateral line rather elevated anteriorly; not over 3 scale rows between lateral line and base of first dorsal fin................24

23b. Lateral line more or less straight; 4 or more scale rows between
lateral line and base of first dorsal fin.....................25

24a. Snout rather blunt; body elongate and slender...............
........SWAMP DARTER, *Etheostoma gracile* (Girard). Fig. 545.
Olivaceous with sides mottled and marked with about 9 blotches;
distance from tip of snout to angle of gill membrane about ½ length
of head. Base of caudal fin with 3 vertical spots. Length 2 inches.
Southern Illinois and Indiana to Mississippi and Texas.

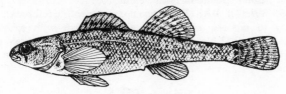

Figure 545

EASTERN SWAMP DARTER, *Etheostoma fusiforme* (Girard). **Fig. 546.**
Olivaceous with blotches along each side which may fuse to form
an irregular lateral band; 3 or 4 spots across base of caudal fin; distance from tip of the snout to the angle of the gill membrane decidedly
greater than ½ the length of the head. Widespread from Massachusetts
to Maryland.

Figure 546

Etheostoma zoniferum (Hubbs and Cannon).
Similar to swamp darter, but gill membranes more closely connected; distance from the tip of snout to angle of gill membrane somewhat greater than ½ the length of head; sides marked anteriorly with
irregular blotches which form about 4 vertical bars on the peduncle;
3 spots across base of caudal fin. Central part of Alabama River
system.

ROUGHCHEEK DARTER, *Etheostoma serriferum* (Hubbs and Cannon).
Similar to the eastern swamp darter, but the lateral line is longer,
reaching to below middle of soft dorsal fin; gill membranes rather

closely connected; distance from tip of snout to angle of the gill membrane is greater than ½ the length of the head; opercle more saw toothed. Sides marked with more or less confluent blotches, 4 spots across base of caudal fin. South and North Carolina and southeastern Virginia.

BROWN DARTER, *Etheostoma edwini* **(Hubbs and Cannon)......**
.....................................(See Fig. 552, couplet 30b.)
Individuals with only 3 rows of scales above lateral line will key here.

24b. Snout rather pointed; body stout.........................CY-
PRESS SWAMP DARTER, *Etheostoma barratti* **(Holbrook). Fig. 547.**
Similar to eastern swamp darter. Brownish with sides mottled and marked with 9-12 blotches; 3 or 4 black spots across base of caudal fin. Length 1½ inches. Widespread in coastal states from Virginia to Louisiana.

Figure 547

SALUDA DARTER, *Etheostoma saludae* **(Hubbs and Cannon).**
Similar to cypress swamp darter. About 10 rectangular blotches along each side and with 3-4 spots across base of caudal fin. Santee River system in South Carolina.
Etheostoma colle **(Hubbs and Cannon).**
Sides marked with median dark stripe breaking into blotches on the peduncle; 3 dark spots across base of caudal fin. Catawba River system, South Carolina.

25a. Gill membranes scarcely connected across isthmus. (See Fig. 516)
..26

25b. Gill membranes more or less connected across isthmus. (See Fig. 518) 33

26a. Shoulder region without a black humeral scale, may have a faint dark spot...27

26b. Shoulder region with a distinctly enlarged black humeral scale.31

27a. Opercle scaleless; cheek may or may not be scaled. GREEN-
THROAT DARTER, *Etheostoma lepidum* (Baird and Girard).....
....Fig. 548
Olivaceous, sides marked with bars. Very similar to rainbow darter,
but head is more naked. Length 2½ inches, Oklahoma south through
Texas.

Figure 548

ORANGETHROAT DARTER, *Etheostoma spectabile* (Agassiz)....
....Fig. 549
Olivaceous with about 10 dark bars on sides. Length 2½ inches.
Eastern Colorado to Ohio and Tennessee.

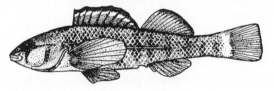

Figure 549

27b. Opercle with scales; cheek may or may not be scaled........28

28a. Cheeks nearly naked; opercles scaled........................29

28b. Cheeks and opercles more or less scaled....................30

29a. Gill membranes not connected across isthmus................
................REDSPOT DARTER, *Etheostoma grahami* (Girard)
Very similar to greenthroat darter except opercle is scaled and
lateral line has more than 50 scales. Males have throat red instead of
blue. Texas and New Mexico.

221

29b. Gill membranes very slightly connected across isthmus. RAIN-
BOW DARTER, *Etheostoma caeruleum* Storer...........Fig. 550
Olivaceous with 10-12 dark bars on each side. Breeding males
very brilliant. Length 2½ inches. Southern Minnesota to eastern Ontario and south to Alabama and Arkansas.

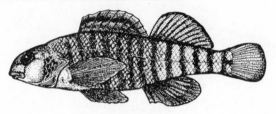

Figure 550

TIPPECANOE DARTER, *Etheostoma tippecanoe* Jordan and Evermann.
Individuals without a dark humeral scale will key here. (See
couplet 31a.)

30a. Lateral line extending on 47 to 53 scales.....................
.................MUD DARTER, *Etheostoma asprigene* (Forbes)
Individuals with a rather complete lateral line will key here. (See
Fig. 540, couplet 20b.)

GULF DARTER, *Etheostoma swaini* (Jordan)....................
....................................(See Fig. 541, couplet 20b.)
Individuals with a more complete lateral line will key here.

EASTERN SWAMP DARTER, *Etheastoma fusiforme* (Girard)......
....................................(See Fig. 546, couplet 24a.)
Individuals with more than 3 rows of scales above lateral line
will key here.

30b. Lateral line very short, usually not extending far behind first
dorsal fin and extending on 13 to 30 scales. IOWA DARTER,
Etheostoma exile (Girard)...........................Fig. 551
Pale olivaceous with 9-11 blotches or vertical bars on each side.
Spawning males very brilliant with red spots on sides and blue and
red bands across dorsal fins. Length 2½ inches. Widely distributed
from southern Canada and Great Lakes drainage through the upper
Mississippi valley from Colorado to Ohio.

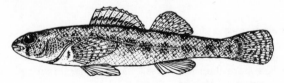

Figure 551

BROWN DARTER, *Etheostoma edwini* (Hubbs and Cannon). Fig. 552.
Grayish brown with 8 or 9 spots along lateral line. Length 2 inches.
Southeastern Alabama, Florida, and southern Georgia.

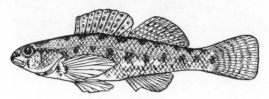

Figure 552

SPRING DARTER, *Etheostoma tuscumbia* Gilbert and Swain.....
....Fig. 553
Greenish, much mottled or speckled and with 8-10 blotches along
lateral line. Length 2 inches. Tributaries of upper Tennessee River in
Alabama and Tennessee.

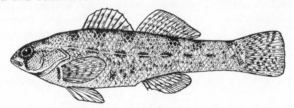

Figure 553

SPOTTAIL DARTER, *Etheostoma squamiceps* Jordan......Fig. 554
Dusky olive with sides mottled sometimes forming about 10 irregular bars. Length 2 inches. Humeral scale present, but may not be
very dark. Indiana southward through western Kentucky and Tennessee to Mississippi.

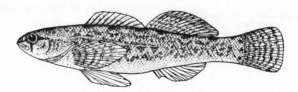

Figure 554

Etheostoma luteovinctum Gilbert and Swain.............Fig. 555
Lateral line on 30-35 scales. Pale olive; 7 dusky bars on back
reaching to lateral line and 9 dusky blotches on each side below

lateral line; black spots at base of caudal fin. Length 2 inches. Upper Tennessee River drainage.

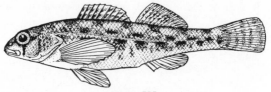

Figure 555

31a. Cheeks almost naked; opercles scaled......................
....**TIPPE-**
CANOE DARTER, *Etheostoma tippecanoe* Jordan and Evermann
Body dusky; marked with fine dots and by 12 cross bars on each side. Length 1½ inches. Northern Indiana and Ohio.

SPOTTAIL DARTER, *Etheostoma squamiceps* Jordan.............
....................................**(See Fig. 554, couplet 30b.)**
Individuals with a dark humeral scale will key here.

ARKANSAS RIVER DARTER, *Etheostoma cragini* Gilbert........
...................................**(See Fig. 556, couplet 32a.)**
Individuals with a few scales on cheeks and opercles will key here.

31b. Cheeks and opercles without scales........................**32**

32a. Snout shorter than diameter of eye. Fig. 556.................
.........**ARKANSAS RIVER DARTER,** *Etheostoma cragini* **Gilbert**
Olivaceous and mottled; speckled below lateral line; 10-12 dusky spots along side; humeral scale black and conspicuous. Length 2 inches. Colorado to Arkansas.

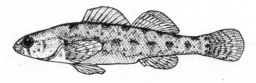

Figure 556

REDFIN DARTER, *Etheostoma whipplei* (Girard).........**Fig. 557**
Grayish and mottled. Males with red spots on sides and with indistinct bars posteriorly. Black humeral scale present. Length 2½

inches. Lower Arkansas River drainage. South to Texas and east to Alabama.

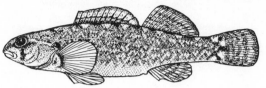

Figure 557

ORANGEBELLY DARTER, *Etheostoma radiosum* (Hubbs and Black).
Very similar to redfin darter, but differs in having more than 62 scale rows instead of less than 61 scales. Southeastern Oklahoma and southern Arkansas.

32b. Snout as long as diameter of eye. SPECKLED DARTER, *Etheostoma punctulatum* (Agassiz)..................................Fig. 558
Dark green; sides finely dotted and mottled. Males with indistinct bars on sides. Length 2 inches. Ozark region of Missouri, Arkansas, and Oklahoma.

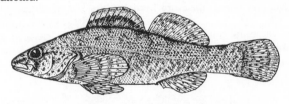

Figure 558

OBEY STREAKED DARTER, *Etheostoma obeyense* Kirsch.
Resembles the fantail darter. Light olive with 10-11 irregular blotches on each side; large humeral scale present. Length 2½ inches. Upper Cumberland River drainage.

CUMBERLAND STREAKED DARTER, *Etheostoma virgatum* (Jordan).
Grayish green with a spot on each scale forming series of longitudinal lines on each side as in fantail darter. Length 2½ inches. Cumberland River drainage, Kentucky.

33a. Lateral line reaching only to front of soft dorsal fin; spinous dorsal fin very low, only about 1/2 height of soft dorsal fin. FANTAIL DARTER, *Etheostoma flabellare* Rafinesque............Fig. 559
Grayish green; body scales each with a spot, sometimes forming longitudinal lines (*E. f. lineolatum* Agassiz, Fig. 560); large black hum-

eral scale present; sides with 9-11 cross bars. Lower jaw more or less projecting. Length 3 inches. Several subspecies from Minnesota to Vermont and south to North Carolina and Oklahoma.

Figure 559

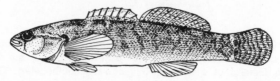

Figure 560

CUMBERLAND FANTAIL DARTER, *Etheostoma kennicotti* (Putnam). Closely resembles fantail darter, but lacks dots, lines, and bars on sides. Upper Cumberland River and adjacent Tennessee River drainages.

33b. Lateral line almost complete or reaching past front of soft dorsal fin; spinous dorsal fin more than 1/2 the height of the soft dorsal fin. Fig. 561.........YOKE DARTER, *Etheostoma juliae* Meek
Dusky olive to greenish; faint yellowish scale dots form irregular longitudinal lines on sides; 5 or 6 faint bars on each side. Length 2½ inches. Southern drainage (White River) of the Ozarks, Missouri.

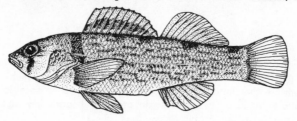

Figure 561

34a. Anal spines 1. Fig. 562.....................................
....SPRING DARTER, *Etheostoma fonticola* (Jordan and Gilbert)

Figure 562

Olivaceous and somewhat mottled with median row of blotches on each side; 3 spots across base of caudal fin. Length 1½ inches. Texas.

34b. Anal spines 2 ....**35**

35a. Cheeks and opercles mostly naked (several scales may be on opercle). Fig. 563 ....

....**LEAST DARTER,** *Etheostoma microperca* Jordan and Gilbert
Olivaceous mottled with brown; pelvic fins very long. Length 1½ inches. Southeastern Manitoba and Great Lakes region to Kentucky and Oklahoma.

Figure 563

35b. Cheeks and opercles completely scaled ....
................**CYPRESS DARTER,** *Etheostoma proeliare* (Hay)
Very similar to least darter; may have several pored scales representing lateral line. Length 1½ inches. Western Tennessee and Arkansas southward to Texas and western Florida.

DRUM or SHEEPSHEAD FAMILY, Sciaenidae

The drum family contains mostly marine species, many of which are important game fishes and may occur in the mouths of rivers along the coasts. The family contains but one strictly freshwater species, the FRESHWATER DRUM, *Aplodinotus grunniens* Rafinesque (Fig. 564) which is widespread, extending from the James Bay drainage in Canada

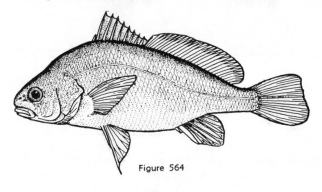

Figure 564

227

through the Great Lakes drainage exclusive of Lake Superior and southward into Mexico. This is a deep bodied silvery fish with a high back and a long dorsal fin. The lateral line extends out onto the caudal fin.

Like many of the marine members of this family, the freshwater drum makes a rumbling noise supposed to be produced by the swim bladder. It feeds mostly on the bottom, grinding its food with a powerful set of flat pharyngeal teeth. It possesses large ivory-like ear bones or ossicles within its skull which are quite unlike those of any other freshwater fish. The freshwater drum reaches a size of 10 pounds and a length of several feet, although much larger sizes were reported in the past century.

Along the Atlantic coast a large number of marine species may enter brackish and freshwater at the mouths of the rivers. The CHANNEL BASS, *Sciaenops ocellatus* (Linnaeus); the SPOT, *Leiostomus xanthurus* Lacépède; the SEA DRUM *Pogonias cromis* (Linnaeus); the CROAKER, *Micropogon undulatus* (Linnaeus); the SEA TROUT, *Cynoscion nebulosus* (Valenciennes); and several others have been reported from fresh and brackish waters along the Atlantic coast.

CICHLID FAMILY, Cichlidae

This family contains many species native to the rivers of Africa and tropical America. One species, the RIO GRANDE CICHLID, *Cichlasoma cyanoguttata* (Baird and Girard) (Fig. 565) extends its range northward into the Rio Grande drainage of Texas. These fishes are

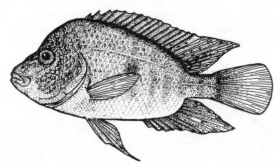

Figure 565

characterized by a broken lateral line and by only one aperture for each nostril. The Rio Grande cichlid has a deep body which is brownish and is speckled all over, including the fins with blue spots. Black spots may occur on the dorsal fin, back, and at the base of the caudal fin. It reaches a length of about 7 inches.

SURF-FISH FAMILY, Embiotocidae

The surf fishes form a large marine group with one species living in freshwater in California. The family is differentiated by numerous characters, of which one of the most outstanding is a sheath of scales separated from the body by a groove and extending along the base of the spiny and soft dorsal fins. The members of this family are live bearers, retaining the eggs in the ducts of the female until the young are fully developed.

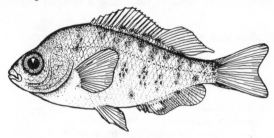

Figure 566

The TULEPERCH, *Hysterocarpus traski* Gibbons (Fig. 566) occurs in the streams of central California, mostly in the drainage of the Sacramento River. It is a small deep bodied fish with a brown back and olivaceous sides. The females are marked on the sides with irregular blotches forming bars. It reaches a length of 4 to 5 inches.

SLEEPER FAMILY, Eleotridae

This family is closely allied to the goby family, but the members of this group are readily distinguished by the pelvic fins which are close together, but are not united to form a sucking disc. The lateral line is absent. Some species live in freshwater in the West Indies and Mexico, and several of these are sometimes found in freshwater close to the sea in the southern States.

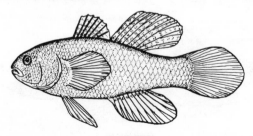

Figure 567

The FAT SLEEPER, *Dormitator maculatus* (Bloch) (Fig. 567) is found in the lower stretches of the rivers from South Carolina to Texas. It has a short heavy body which is brown with light spots. The maxillary reaches to the anterior margin of the orbit. It reaches a length of over 12 inches.

The SPINYCHEEK SLEEPER, *Eleotris pisonis* (Gmelin) is usually found in fresh and brackish water, rather than in the sea, along the Gulf of Mexico. It has a rather elongated body which is brown. The maxillary reaches to the back of the orbit. It reaches a length of 6 to 7 inches.

Several other sleepers are reported from freshwater in southern Florida.

GOBY FAMILY, Gobiidae

Gobies are essentially a marine group mostly found in the shallow water along the sea shores where several species may enter the mouths of rivers. Most gobies are small, usually about 2-3 inches long, but several species may reach a length of over 12 inches. They have large pectoral fins and have no lateral line. They can be readily distinguished by a ventral sucker disc formed by the fusion of the pelvic fins. (Fig. 568).

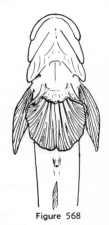

Figure 568

A number of species, including the SPOTTED GOBY, *Gobius stigmaticus* (Poey) (Fig. 569) may occasionally enter freshwater along the coasts of the southern Atlantic and the Gulf of Mexico. It reaches a length of about 5 inches. The FRESH-WATER GOBY, *Gobionella shufeldti* (Jordan and Eigenmann) (Fig. 570) seems to be confined to freshwater in the lower stretches of streams emptying into the Gulf of Mexico. It reaches a length of about 4 inches. Several species of MUDSUCKERS, *Gillichthys* (Fig. 571) and the TIDEWATER GOBY, *Eucyclogobius newberryi* (Girard) may enter freshwater in California.

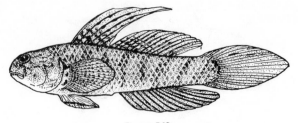

Figure 569

230

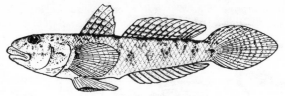

Figure 570

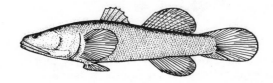

Figure 571

SCULPIN FAMILY, Cottidae

The sculpin family is primarily marine, but a number of species are restricted to freshwater. The freshwater forms are characterized by large flat heads and rather slender bodies. The eyes are located on the upper surface of the head and are close together. The pectoral fins are very much enlarged. The soft rays are seldom branched except in the caudal fin, and care must be taken to distinguish them from the spines. One of the diagnostic characters is the spines on the edge of the preopercle of most species. These are covered by skin, but can be detected by close scrutiny or by dissection. Sculpins are without scales but may be covered by tiny prickles.

Sculpins are bottom fishes hiding under rocks during the day, either in swift streams or along rocky shores of cold lakes of the mountains or the northern United States. They feed on a wide variety of aquatic animals including small fishes. Sculpins prepare a nest where the eggs are suspended on the underside of logs or stones and are guarded by the male. Most species are colored a grayish or olive brown and mottled with dark brown to black. The species are well defined east of the Rockies, but are not as clearly defined west of the Rockies, where much variation occurs in different river systems.

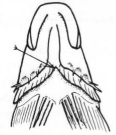

Figure 572

1a. Gill membranes (Fig. 572) free from isthmus. Fig. 573.....DEEP-
WATER SCULPIN, *Myoxocephalus (Triglopsis) thompsoni* (Girard)

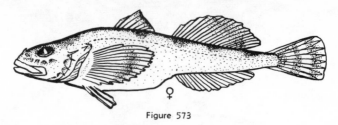

Figure 573

Pale brown or cream color. Males with very large soft dorsal fin
(Fig. 574). Length 6 inches. Deep waters of the Great Lakes and the
same or a similar form in streams of arctic America.

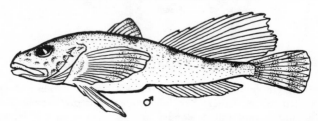

Figure 574

1b. Gill membranes (Fig. 575) attached to wide
part of isthmus..........................2

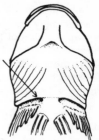

2a. Preopercular spines absent. Fig. 576......
.....*Cottus leiopomus* Gilbert and Evermann
Grayish olive and mottled; lateral line complete; body smooth without prickles. Length 3-4
inches. Wood River, Shoshone, Idaho.

Figure 575

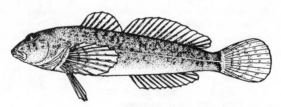

Figure 576

2b. One or more preopercular spines present (See Figs. 580, 583) and usually well developed 3

3a. Pelvic fin with 1 spine and 4 rays, spine is enclosed and hidden in same sheath with outer ray. Fig. 577...............4

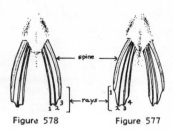

Figure 578   Figure 577

3b. Pelvic fin with 1 spine and 3 rays, spine is enclosed and hidden in same sheath with outer ray. Fig. 578.......................7

4a. Preopercular spine sickle-shape or strongly curved upward. Fig. 579.................**SPOONHEAD SCULPIN,** *Cottus ricei* (Nelson)
Body grayish and deeply blotched; heavily covered with prickles. Length 3 inches. Shores of Great Lakes and northward in Canada, west of Hudson Bay.

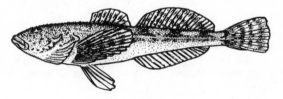

Figure 579

4b. Preopercular spine not sickle-shape or not strongly curved but more or less straight...5

Figure 580

5a. One large preopercular spine present (Fig. 580) and no smaller spines below it. **ALEUTIAN SCULPIN,** *Cottus aleuticus* Gilbert...
....Fig. 581
Light brown and mottled; lateral line rather complete, sometimes drops abruptly below end of soft dorsal fin; posterior nostril tubular;

anal fin shorter than dorsal fin. Length 3 inches. Coastal streams, Monterey, California to Alaska.

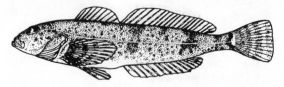

Figure 581

SMOOTH SCULPIN, *Cottus beldingi* **Eigenmann and Eigenmann.**
....Fig. 582
Grayish and mottled; posterior nostril not tubular. Columbia River drainage east of the Cascades to Lake Lahonton.

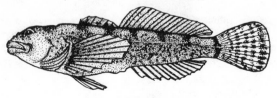

Figure 582

Cottus annae **Jordan and Starks.**
Similar to the smooth sculpin, but has a poorly developed blunt spine below the large preopercular spine. Lower Colorado River drainage.

KLAMATH SCULPIN, *Cottus klamathensis* **Gilbert.**
Olive brown and blotched; posterior nostril tubular; lateral line more or less incomplete. Klamath River system, Oregon and northern California.

SNAKE RIVER SCULPIN, *Cottus tubulatus* **Hubbs and Schultz.**
Similar to smooth sculpin except all nostrils are tubular. Snake River drainage, Idaho.

Cottus princeps **Gilbert.**
Dorsal fins well united; preopercular spines much reduced, may be absent. Upper Klamath Lake, Oregon.

5b. **One large preopercular spine present with 2 small spines below (Fig. 583), spines are usually covered and hidden by skin** 6

Figure 583

6a. Lateral line not complete but extending only to below middle of soft dorsal fin. NORTHERN SCULPIN, *Cottus bairdi* Girard.Fig. 584
Dark brown to grayish olive and mottled; spiny dorsal fin with black spot posteriorly. Length 6-7 inches. Widespread from southern Canada to southern Appalachians and the Ozarks. Represented in the west by *C. b. semiscaber* (Cope) in the Bonneville Basin; *C. b. punctulatus* (Gill) in the Rocky Mountain area, and by *C. b. shasta* Jordan and Starks in the Sacramento drainage.

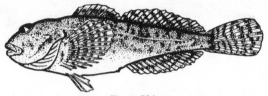

Figure 584

Cottus gulosus (Girard). Fig. 585.
In the coastal streams of California northward. Closely resembles the northern sculpin. *Cottus perplexus* Gilbert and Evermann in Washington and Oregon is similar.

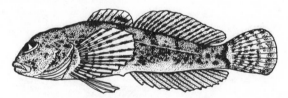

Figure 585

6b. Lateral line more or less complete, extending past soft dorsal fin.
Cottus rhotheus (Rosa Smith).........................Fig. 586
Dark gray and darkly speckled or mottled; dorsal fins separated by small space. Length 3-4 inches. Lower Columbia River and Puget Sound drainages.

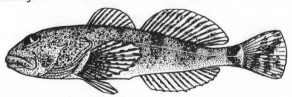

Figure 586

235

PRICKLY SCULPIN, *Cottus asper* **Richardson. Fig. 587.**

Grayish olive and mottled; black spot in posterior part of spiny dorsal fin; dorsal fins confluent; body very prickly. Length up to 12 inches. Coastal streams from Ventura County, California to Alaska.

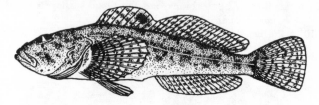

Figure 587

COLUMBIA SCULPIN, *Cottus hubbsi* **Bailey and Dimick.**

Mottled dorsal fins separated by notch; not very prickly. Columbia River drainage of Washington and Idaho.

TENNESSEE SCULPIN, *Cottus carolinae* **(Gill). Fig. 588.**

Grayish brown and mottled. Similar to northern sculpin but has a more complete lateral line; pectoral rays number 16 instead of 14-15. Length 4 inches. Upper Tennessee River drainage to the Ozarks in southern Missouri.

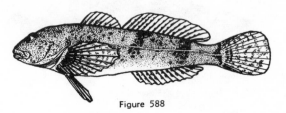

Figure 588

7a. One large preopercular spine with no smaller spines below......
.....................ROUGH SCULPIN, *Cottus asperrimus* **Rutter**
Grayish olive and mottled; body heavily prickled; lateral line incomplete. Sacramento and San Joaquin River drainages.
Cottus greenei **(Gilbert and Culver).**
Very incomplete lateral line. Snake River, Idaho.

7b. One large preopercular spine with 1 or 2 smaller spines below...8

8a. Anal rays 11 to 12. Fig. 589....................................
...................SLIMY SCULPIN, *Cottus cognatus* **Richardson**
Olive brown with dark blotches; lateral line incomplete. Widely distributed from Great Lakes Region northward into Alaska. Isolated

populations in southeastern Minnesota and northwestern Iowa and in the Potomac River and James River drainages.

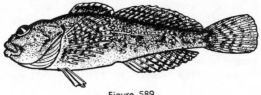

Figure 589

8b. Anal rays 14 to 15...........*Cottus tenuis* (Evermann and Meek)
Dark brown with blotches; lateral line incomplete. Some pectoral rays branched; smooth to slightly prickled. Length 3 inches. Klamath Lakes, Oregon.

Cottus marginatus **(Bean).**
Brownish with blotches; a blunt spine appearing as a lobe, is below the large preopercular spine; lateral line incomplete. Walla Walla River, Washington.

FLATFISH FAMILY, Bothidae

The flatfish family contains a number of species on the Atlantic and Pacific coasts, several of which sometimes enter the mouths of rivers along the Atlantic coast. The SAND DAB, *Citharichthys spilopterus* Gunther (Fig. 590), is occasionally found in freshwater from New York to Texas. It is olive brown with dark blotches and reaches a length of 5-6 inches. The jaws are equal on both sides. Another small flatfish

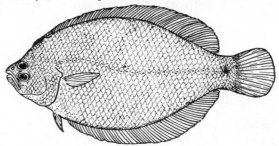

Figure 590

occasionally entering freshwater is the FRINGED FLOUNDER, *Etropus crossotus* Jordan and Gilbert distributed from Virginia southward. It is olive brown with dark blotches, but has unequal jaws. The opercle on the blind side has a distinct white fringe along the margin. It reaches a length of almost 6 inches.

FLOUNDER FAMILY, Pleuronectidae

This is a large and abundant marine group widely distributed on both coasts. Several species, especially the young, may enter rivers for a short distance. On the east coast from New York to Texas, the SOUTHERN FLOUNDER, *Paralichthys lethostigma* Jordan and Gilbert is sometimes found in freshwater. It is dusky olive with some darker spots and may reach a large size, 2 to 3 feet in length. The STARRY FLOUNDER, *Platichthys stellatus* Pallas (Fig. 591) is widely distributed along

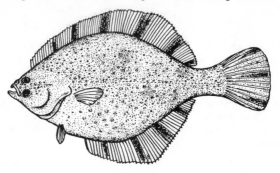

Figure 591

the Pacific coast and may enter rivers. It is characterized by 4 or 5 prominent vertical black bands in both the dorsal and anal fins. It is commonly 12 to 15 inches in length but may reach a much larger size.

SOLE FAMILY, Achiridae

This family contains small flatfishes which have the pectoral fins poorly developed, or have one or both fins absent. Several species may

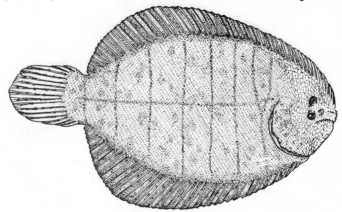

Figure 592

enter the mouths or rivers along the Atlantic coast. They are usually 5 to 6 inches in length. The HOGCHOKER, *Achirus maculatus* (Bloch) (Fig. 592) is common along most of the Atlantic coast. It is brown with about 8 dark cross bars. Only the right pectoral fin is present. Along the southern Atlantic and Gulf coasts, the LINED SOLE, *Achirus lineatus* (Linnaeus) sometimes enters freshwater. It is dark with about 8 cross bars. Both pectoral fins are absent.

SOME USEFUL LITERATURE
FOR THE IDENTIFICATION OF FISHES

Bailey, Reeve M., Winn, Howard Elliott, and Smith, C. Lavett. 1955. Fishes from the Escambia River, Alabama and Florida, with Ecologic and Taxonomic Notes. Proc. Acad. Nat. Sci. Phila., Vol. CVI: 109-164. Description of the fishes of a previously little known region.

Berg, Leo S. 1940. Classification of Fishes, Both Recent and Fossil. Trav. Inst. Zool. Acad. Sci. U. R. S. S. Tome 5, Livr. 2: pp. 87-517. A very modern classification of the fishes of the world to families with some illustrations, but no keys

Carl, G. Clifford, and Clemens, W. A. 1953. The Freshwater Fishes of British Columbia. British Columbia Prov. Mus., Handbook No. 5, Ed. 2: 136 pp. Keys and illustrations of the fishes of British Columbia.

Carr, Archie, and Goin, Coleman I. 1955. Guide to the Reptiles, Amphibians and Fresh-Water Fishes of Florida. Univ. Florida Press, Gainesville. i-viii, 341 pp. Keys, ranges, and descriptions of fishes found in freshwaters of Florida with some illustrations.

Eddy, Samuel, and Surber, Thaddeus. 1947. Northern Fishes with Special Reference to the Upper Mississippi Valley, Univ. of Minn. Press, Mpls., Rev. Ed., 276 pp. Keys and Descriptions of the fishes of Minnesota with illustrations.

Forbes, Stephen A., and Richardson, Robert E. 1920. The Fishes of Illinois. Second Edit. Nat. Hist. Surv. Ill., Vol. 3: cxxi, 357 pp. Atlas, 103 maps. Keys and descriptions of the fishes of Illinois with illustrations. Nomenclature not up to date.

Fowler, H. W. 1945. A study of the Fishes of the Southern Piedmont and Coastal Plain. Acad. Nat. Sci. Philadelphia, Monogr. No. 7, 408 pp.

Gunter, Gordon. 1942. A list of the Fishes of the Mainland of North and Middle America Recorded from Both Freshwater and Sea Water. Am. Midl. Nat., Vol. 28: pp. 305-356. A list of the marine fishes known to enter freshwater and the freshwater fishes entering salt water. No keys or illustrations.

Harlan, James R., and Speaker, Everett B. 1951. Iowa Fishes and Fishing. Iowa State Cons. Comm., Des Moines. 237 pp. Keys and description of fishes of Iowa with excellent illustrations.

Hubbs, Carl L., and Lagler, Karl F. 1947. Fishes of the Great Lakes Region. Cranbrook Instit. Sci., Bull. 26; xi, 186 pp. Keys and ranges of fishes of the Great Lakes drainage with illustrations.

Jordan, David S. 1929. A Manual of the Vertebrate Animals of the Northern United States. 13th ed. World Book Co., Yonkers-on-Hudson, N. Y., 446 pp. Keys to the fishes of the northeastern United States.

Jordan, David S., and Evermann, Barton W 1896-1900. The Fishes of North and Middle America. Bull. U. S. Nat. Mus., No. 47, in 4 parts, 3313 pp. Out of date but still the classical work covering all marine fishes and freshwater fishes of North America known at the time of publication. With keys, ranges, descriptions and some illustrations.

Jordan, David S., and Evermann, Barton W. 1905. American Food and Game Fishes. Doubleday, Page and Co., N. Y., 572 pp. A popular account of American marine and freshwater game and food fishes with keys, descriptions and illustrations.

Jordan, David S., Barton Warren, and Clark, Howard Walton. 1930. Check List of the Fishes and Fishlike Vertebrates of North and Middle America North of the Northern Boundary of Venezuela and Columbia. Rept. U. S. Comm. Fish., 1928, Pt. 2: iv, 670 pp. A complete list of names for all species with synonyms for both marine and freshwater fishes. Many species are invalid and nomenclature is not up to date. No keys or illustrations.

Knapp, Frank T. 1953. Fishes Found in the Fresh Waters of Texas. Ragland Studio and Litho. Printing Co., Brunswick, Georgia. viii, 166 pp. A description of the fishes of Texas with range and keys. Illustrated.

Koelz, Walter. 1929. Coregonid Fishes of the Great Lakes. Bull. U. S. Bur. Fish., Vol. 43, 1927; Pt. 2: pp. 297-643. Detailed descriptions of all coregonid fishes inhabiting the Great Lakes with illustrations.

Koelz, Walter. 1931. Coregonid Fishes of Northeastern North America. Papers Mich. Acad. Sci., Arts, and Letters, Vol. 13, 1930: pp. 303-432. Detailed descriptions of the coregonid fishes found in waters other than the Great Lakes in northeastern North America.

Kuhne, Eugene R. 1939. A Guide to the Fishes of Tennessee and the Mid-south. Tenn. Dept. Cons., Nashville. 124 pp. Keys and descriptions for most of the fishes found in Tennessee. Illustrated.

LaMonte, Francesca. 1945. North American Game Fishes. Doubleday, Doran, Garden City. xiv, 202 pp. Descriptions and ranges of salt and freshwater game fishes with keys and record weights and lengths. Illustrated.

Legendre, Vianney. 1952. Clef des poissons de peche sportive et commerciale de la Province de Quebec. Ministre de la Chasse et des pecheries, Quebec. 84 pp.

Legendre, Vianney. 1954. Volume 1. Key to Game and Commercial Fishes of the Province of Quebec. Game and Fisheries Dept., Province of Quebec, Montreal. pp. 180. Illustrated. Includes 101 species.

Massman, William H. 1954. Marine Fishes in Fresh and Brackish Waters of Virginia Rivers. Ecology, Vol. 35, No. 1: pp. 75-78. No keys or illustrations.

Nichols, John T. 1942. Representative North American Fresh-water Fishes. Macmillan, New York. 128 pp. Descriptions, ranges, and habits of 60 representative North American Fishes. Illustrated but no keys.

Pratt, Henry S. 1935. A manual of Land and Fresh Water Vertebrate Animals of the United States (Exclusive of Birds). 2nd ed. P. Blakiston's Son and Co., Philadelphia. 416 pp. Keys and descriptions of representative species of various genera of fishes. Nomenclature not up to date.

Schrenkeisen, Ray. 1938. Field Book of Fresh-water Fishes of North America North of Mexico. G. P. Putnam's Sons, New York. xii — 312 pp. Description and ranges of the freshwater fishes of the United States attempting to list all species many of which are not considered valid. Nomenclature not up to date. No keys. Illustrated.

Schultz, Leonard P. 1936. Keys to the Fishes of Washington, Oregon and Closely Adjoining Regions. Univ. Wash. Publ. Zool. Vol. 2, No. 4; pp. 103-228. Useful for identification of both marine and freshwater fishes of this region.

Scott, W. B. 1954. Freshwater Fishes of Eastern Canada. Univ. Toronto Press, Toronto. 144 pp. Popular descriptions, habits, and ranges of 142 species of fishes of eastern Canada. No keys. Illustrated.

Simon, James R. 1946. Wyoming Fishes. Bull. Wyo. Game and Fish Dept., Cheyenne. No. 4, 129 pp. Descriptions of Wyoming fishes with keys. Illustrated.

Smith, Hugh M. 1907. The Fishes of North Carolina. North Carolina Geol. and Econ. Surv. Vol. 2: xi — 453 pp. Although out of date, still the most authoritative account of the fishes of this region.

INDEX AND PICTURED-GLOSSARY

A

ABDOMINAL: referring to belly region or underside of body between breast and anus. 8
Achiridae 24, 238
Achirus 239
  lineatus 239
  maculatus 239
Acipenser 34
  brevirostris 37
  fulvescens 37
  medirostris 36
  oxyrhynchus 36
  transmontanus 35
Acipenseridae 16, 64
Acrocheilus 82
  alutaceum 82
Adinia 166
  xenica 166
ADIPOSE FIN: see fin. 10, 17. Figs. 2, 601
ADIPOSE MEMBRANE: membrane covering the surface of the eyeball except for a vertical slit. 21, 41. Figs. 39, 593

Figure 593

Agnatha 1
Agonostomus 179
  monticola 179
Agosia 90
  chrysogaster 90
AIR BLADDER: see swim bladder. 38, 39
Alabama chubsucker 69
Alabama shad 44
Aleutian sculpin 233
Alewife 44
Allegheny brook lamprey 34
Alligator gar 39
Alosa 43
  aestivalis 44
  alabamae 44
  chrysochloris 43
  mediocris 44
  ohiensis 43
  pseudoharengus 44
  sapidissima 43
Amazon molly 176
Ambloplites 189
  rupestris 189
Amblyopsidae 23, 160
Amblyopsis 160
  rosae 160
  spelaea 160
Ameiuridae 147
Ameiurus 149
American eel 155
American grayling 57

American shad 43
American smelt 58
Amia 38
  calva 38
Amiidae 16, 38
AMMOCOETES: larval lampreys. 29
Ammocrypta 197
  asprella 197
  beani 198
  clara 198
  pellucida 198
  vivax 198
ANADROMOUS: fishes living in the sea and entering freshwater to spawn. 2
ANAL FIN: see fin. 9 Fig. 601
Anchoa 46
  hepsetus 46
  mitchilli 46
Anchovy 46
Anchovy family 18, 45
Anguilla 155
  rostrata 155
Anguillidae 16, 155
ANTERIOR: the front end or toward the front. 7
ANUS: posterior opening of digestive tract. 8 Fig. 2
Apeltes 159
  quadracus 159
Aphredoderidae 25, 178
Aphredoderus 178
  sayanus 178
Aplodinotus 227
  grunniens 227
Archoplites 190
  interruptus 190
Arkansas River darter 224
Arkansas River shiner 145
Arkansas sand darter 198
Arrow darter 218
Ash Meadows springfish 165
Ashy darter 218
Astyanax 64
  fasciatus 64
Atherinidae 21, 180
Atlantic needlefish 156
Atlantic salmon 49
Atlantic sturgeon 36
AXILLARY PROCESS: elongate structure at base of pelvic fin. 10 Fig. 594

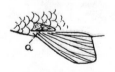

Figure 594

B

Bagre 147
  marinus 147
Banded darter 213
Banded killifish 170, 175
Banded pygmy sunfish 184
Banded sunfish 188

BARBEL: thread-like structure (a) on head, usually near mouth; may be a short minute structure at end of maxillary. 12, 88 Fig. 595

Figure 595

Bass family 27, 181
Bay anchovy 46
Bayou killifish 172
Bear Lake whitefish 46
BELLY: region on underside of fish between pectoral fins and anus. 8
Belonidae 22, 156
BICUSPID: fish tooth with 2 points. 32
Bigeye herring 41
Bigeye redhorse 73
Bigeye sculpin 234
Bigeye shiner 137
Bigheaded darter 204
Bigmouth shiner 139
Black buffalofish 66
Black bullhead 151
Black crappie 186
Black redhorse 73
Blackbanded darter 206
Blackbanded sunfish 187
Blackchin shiner 129
Blackfin 54
Blackfin shiner 118, 130
Blacknose dace 84
Blacknose shiner 129, 138
Blackside darter 205
Blackside snubnose darter 213
Blackspot shiner 141, 143
Blackspotted topminnow 173
Blackstripe topminnow 173
Blacktail redhorse 74
Blacktail shiner 113
Bleeding shiner 132
Blenny darter 212, 215
Blindfish 161
Blue catfish 148
Blue chub 98
Blue sucker 65
Blueback salmon 48
Blueback trout 52
Bluebreasted darter 216
Bluefin 54
Bluegill 194
Bluespotted sunfish 188
Bluestripe darter 203
Bluntface shiner 119
Bluntnose darter 210
Bluntnose minnow 99
Bluntnose shiner 134, 136
Bonneville whitefish 57
Bony fishes 1
Bonytail chub 96
Bothidae 24, 237
Bowfin family 16, 38

BRANCHIOSTEGAL MEM-BRANE: membrane (a) connecting gill cover or opercle with throat. 12 Fig. 596

Figure 596

BRANCHIOSTEGAL RAYS: slender bones (b) in branchiostegal or gill membrane (a) below the gill cover or opercle. 13 Fig. 596

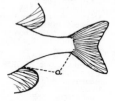

Figure 597

INDEX

Crystal darter 197
CTENOID SCALE: bony scale characterized by tiny spines on exposed surface. 10 Fig. 598

Figure 598

Cumberland fantail darter 226
Cumberland snubnose darter **209**
Cumberland streaked darter 225
Cutlips minnow 86
Cutthroat trout 49
Cycleptus 65
  elongatus 65
CYCLOID SCALE: bony scale characterized by smooth surface. 10 Fig. 599

Figure 599

Cyclostomes 1, 28
Cynoscion 228
  nebulosus 228
Cypress darter 226
Cypress minnow 103
Cypress swamp darter 220
Cyprinidae 20, 79
Cyprinodon 163
  bovinus 164
  diabolis 165
  elegans 164
  hubbsi 163
  macularius **164**
  nevadensis **164**
  radiosus 165
  rubrofluviatilis 164
  salinus 165
  variegatus 163
Cyprinodontidae 23, 161
Cyprinus 80
  carpio 80

D

Daily movements 5
Darters 201
Deepwater sculpin 232
Deltistes 78
  luxatus 78
DENTARIES: largest pair of bones in lower jaw. 12
DEPTH: vertical distance through head or body, usually refers to greatest depth. 13 Fig. 1
Desert cyprinodon 164
Desert minnow 83, 85, 93, 105
Devils Hole cyprinodon 165
Diamond killifish 166
Dionda 102
  episcopa 102
  nubila 102
Dog salmon 48
Dogfish 38
Dollar sunfish 191
Dolly Varden trout 52
Dormitator 230
  maculatus 320
Dorosoma 42
  cepedianum 42
  petenense 43
DORSAL: referring to back or top side. 7
DORSAL FIN: see fin. 9
Drum family 28, 227
Dusky darter 206

E

Eastern brook lamprey 31
Eastern brook trout 51
Eastern longnose sucker 77
Eastern mudminnow 60
Eastern piedmont chub 107
Eastern redbelly dace 91
Eastern redhorse 73
Eastern swamp darter 219, 222
Eastern troutperch 178
Eel 155
Elassoma 184
  evergladei 184
  zonatum 184
Eleotridae 18, 27, 229
Eleotris 230
  pisonis 230
Elops 41
  saurus 41
Embiotocidae 26, 229
Emerald shiner, 127, 135
Empetrichthys 165
  latos 165
  merriami 165
Engraulidae 18, 45
Enneacanthus 187
  chaetodon 187
  gloriosus 188
  obesus 188
Entosphenus 30
  tridentatus 30
Eremichthys 83
  acros 83
Ericymba 101
  buccata 101
Erimyzon 68
  oblongus 68
  succetta 68
  tenuis 69

Esocidae 22, 61
Esox 62
  americanus 63
  lucius 62
  masquinongy 62
  niger 63
  vermiculatus 63
Etheostoma 199, 207
  asprigene 217, 222
  atripinne 209
  barratti 220
  blennioides 209
  blennius 212, 215
  caeruleum 217, 222
  camurum 216
  chlorosomum 210
  cinereum 218
  colle 220
  coosae 216
  cragini 224
  duryi 213
  edwini 220, 223
  euzonum 212
  exile 222
  flabellare 225
  fonticola 226
  fricksium 213, 217
  fusiforme 219, 222
  gracile 219
  grahami 221
  gutselli 212
  histrio 214
  inscriptum 215
  jordani 215
  juliae 213, 226
  kanawhae 212
  kennicotti 226
  lepidum 221
  longimanum 210
  luteovinctum 223
  maculatum 218
  mariae 215
  microperca 227
  nianguae 216
  nigrum 210
  obeyense 225
  osburni 211
  parvipinne 211
  perlongum 208
  podostemone 209
  proeliare 227
  punctulatum 225
  radiosum 225
  ruflineatum 217
  rupestre 214
  sagitta 218
  saludae 220
  serriferum 219
  simoterum 209, 213
  spectabile 221
  spilotum 218
  squamiceps 223, 224
  stigmaeum 208
  swaini 217
  swannanoa 212, 214
  tetrazonum 214
  thalassinum 215
  tippecanoe 222, 224
  tuscumbia 223
  variatum 211
  virgatum 225
  vitreum 207
  whipplei 215, 224
  zonale 213
  zoniferum 219
Etheostomatinae 196
Etropus 237
  crossotus 237
Eucalia 158
  inconstans 158

245

Figure 600

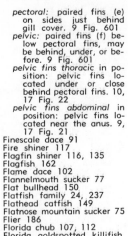

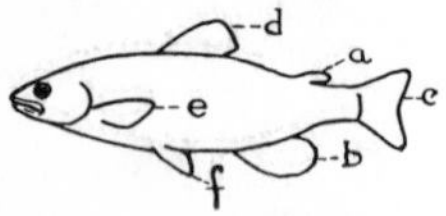

G

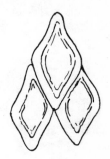

Figure 603

Figure 601

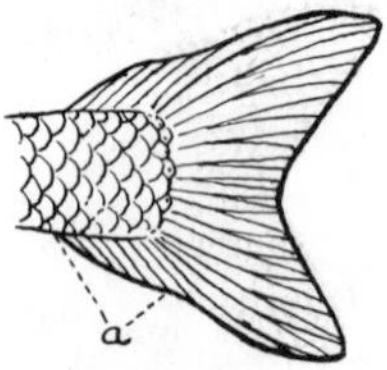

Figure 602

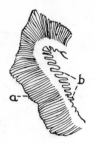

Figure 604

Figure 605

H

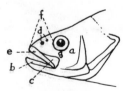

Figure 606

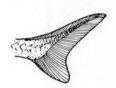

Figure 607

Figure 608

Figure 609

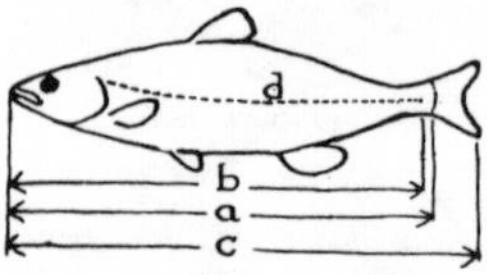

INDEX

Megalopidae 4, 18
Megalops 41
  atlantica 41
Membras 180
  vagrans 180
Menidia 180
  audens 180
  beryllina 180
Mexican tetra 64
Microgadus 157
  tomcod 157
Micropogon 228
  undulatus 228
Micropterus 184
  coosae 185
  dolomieui 185
  notius 185
  punctulatus 185
  salmoides 184
  treculi 185
Mimic shiner 122, 139
Minnow family 20, 79
Mirror shiner 121
Mississippi silversides 180
Missouri saddled darter 214
Mitchills anchovy 46
Moapa 85, 93
  coriacea 85, 93
Mohave chub 94
Molienisia 176
  formosa 176
  latipinna 176
Mongrel buffalofish 66
Mooneye family 18, 44
Mosquitofish 176
Mountain mullet 179
Mountain suckers 74
Moxostoma 71
  anisurum 71
  ariommum 72
  aureolum 71
  breviceps 72
  carinatum 73
  cervinum 72
  collapsum 71
  congestum 72
  conus 72
  coregonus 71
  crassilabre 73
  duquesni 73
  erythrurum 73
  lachneri 72
  lachrymale 73
  macrolepidotum 73
  pappillosum 73
  poecilurum 74
  robustum 73
  rupiscartes 72
  valenciennsei 73
Mud darter 217, 222
Mud pickerel 63
Mudminnow family 22, 60
Mudsuckers 230
Mugil 179
  cephalus 179
  curema 179
Mugilidae 21, 27, 179
Mullet family 21, 27, 179
Mummichog 169
Muskellunge 62
Mylocheilus 89
  caurinus 89
Mylopharodon 85
  conocephalus 85
MYOMERE: segment of body
  or trunk muscles. 33
Myoxocephalus 232
  thompsoni 232

N

NAPE: region of back just
  behind head. 8
Needlefish family 22, 156
Nevada bonytail chub 98
Nevada cyprinodon 164
Niangua darter 216
Night surf smelt 59
Ninespine stickleback 158
NON-PROTRACTILE PRE-
  MAXILLARY: not capable
  of extending forward, pre-
  maxillary not completely
  separated from snout by
  a groove but connected
  by a fleshy bridge or fre-
  num (c). 83, 201, 208
  Fig. 610

Figure 610

Northern brook lamprey 33
Northern chub 106
Northern pike 62
Northern plains minnow 103
Northern redbelly dace 91
Northern redhorse 71
Northern sand darter 198
Northern sculpin 235
NOSTRILS: pair of blind pits
  on snout, each usually
  with an excurrent and an
  incurrent opening.
Notemigonus 92
  chrysoleucas 92
Notropis 102, 113
  albeolus 118, 131
  alburus 143
  altipinnis 115
  amabilis 146
  amnis 140
  amoenus 128
  analostanus 120
  anogenus 130
  ardens 125
  ariommus 127, 128, 132
  asperifrons 124, 141
  atherinoides 128, 135
  atrocaudalis 141, 143
  baileyi 143
  bairdi 141
  bellus 118, 130
  bifrenatus 122, 129
  blennius 138
  boops 137
  braytoni 114
  brazusensis 146
  buchanani 139
  caeruleus 147
  callisema 146
  callistius 136
  callitaenia 147
  camurus 119
  cerasinus 117, 131
  chalybaeus 144

chihuahua 140
chiliticus 123
chlorocephalus 123
chrosomus 143, 144
cocogenis 132, 136
cornutus 117, 131
cummingsae 135
dorsalis 139
euryzonus 116
fumeus 125
galacturus 131, 136
girardi 145
greenei 145
heterodon 129
heterolepis 129, 138
hudsonius 145
hypselopterus 115, 133
hypsilepis 123, 142
illecebrosus 131
jemezanus 128, 135
kanawha 135
leedsi 115, 147
leuciodus 124
lirus 126
longirostris 121
lutipinnis 146
lutrensis 118
maculatus 125
micropteryx 127
niveus 125, 133
notatus 113
ortenburgeri 126, 138
oxyrhynchus 134
ozarcanus 121
perpallidus 127, 128
petersoni 142
photogenis 127
potteri 142
procne 122, 143
prosperinus 137
pyrrhomelas 117
roseipinnis 126
rubellus 129
rubricroceus 131, 137
sabinae 136
scabriceps 138
scepticus 134
signipinnis 116, 135
simus 134, 137
spectrunculus 121
stigmaturus 113
stilbius 123
stonei 116, 133
stramineus 138
texanus 124, 141, 142
topeka 115, 143
trichroistius 120, 132
umbratilis 119, 133
venustus 113, 140, 147
volucellus 122, 139
whipplei 120
xaenocephalus 123, 141,
  144
xaenurus 133
zonatus 132
zonistius 114, 115

Noturus 151
  eleutheris 154
  exilis 153
  flavus 151
  funebris 153
  furiosus 155
  gilberti 154
  gyrinus 152
  hildebrandi 154
  insignis 153
  leptocanthus 152
  miurus 154

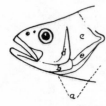

Figure 611

Figure 612

Figure 613

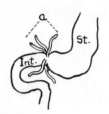

Figure 614

Q

Figure 615

INDEX